STELLER
of the NORTH

STELLER
of the NORTH

by ANN *and* MYRON SUTTON

illustrated by LEONARD EVERETT FISHER

RAND McNALLY & COMPANY

New York • CHICAGO • San Francisco

for
M I C H A E L
and
L A R R Y

CONTENTS

INTRODUCTION   9

1 · YOUNG GEORG WILHELM   11

2 · THE UNKNOWN   24

3 · ST. PETERSBURG   40

4 · SIBERIA   54

5 · AVATCHA BAY   68

6 · THE PACIFIC   79

7 · ALASKA   98

8 · KAYAK ISLAND   112

9 · SHUMAGIN'S ISLAND   123

10 · INDIANS   138

11 · SHIPWRECK   145

12 · DIGGING IN   159

13 · WINTER 172

14 · THE WILD ISLAND 185

15 · HOMEWARD BOUND 199

16 · THE LAST TRAIL 210

FOR FURTHER READING 221

INDEX 223

ILLUSTRATIONS

Capercaillie bird   14

Windsheim   16

Wild Boar   18

Potentilla   20

map: From Windsheim to Berlin, Germany   33

map: From Danzig, Germany to Moscow, Russia   52

Yellow-flowered rhododendron   60

map: Steller's trip across Russia   62

map: Kamchatka, starting point of expedition   73

The "St. Peter" and the "St. Paul"   75

map: Theoretical location of De Gama Land   82

Alaskan sea otter   102

Route of "St. Peter" from Kamchatka to Shumagin Islands   108

Steller's blue jay   121

Steller's sea lion 126

Sketch of Shumagin's Island 135

Alaskan in a baidarka 140

Route of "St. Peter" from Shumagin Islands
to Bering Island 153

Arctic foxes 164

map: North Pacific region, showing route of
Bering's expedition 179

Steller's sea arch on Bering Island 184

Fur seals 187

Spectacled cormorant 191

Northern sea cow 194

Finding the leak 203

map: Discoveries made by "St. Paul" 216

map: Discoveries made by "St. Peter" 217

INTRODUCTION

This story is true. It tells of Captain Vitus Bering's last voyage of discovery through the raging North Pacific Ocean in search of America.

It was an amazing voyage, partly because there were any survivors at all. Only half of the expedition returned, and then only after a heroic battle against great hardships and enormous misfortune.

Surprisingly, the hero of that adventure was not a seaman at all, but a brilliant and stubborn young naturalist who, more than anyone else, brought the survivors of the expedition back alive. Not only that, he returned with the first news and descriptions of some of the most unusual wild animals on the face of the earth.

This man was Georg Wilhelm Steller.

His life began more than 250 years ago, which means that today some of the facts about him have been lost, and there are no pictures of him in existence. Little is known of his early years. What we do know has been pieced together from fragments of fact, combined with the known customs of the eighteenth century.

Other parts of Steller's life are better known, and were so eventful that a description of them would require several books. We have therefore left out many of his experiences, and have bridged these gaps with conversation based on the actual historical record.

That record was gathered chiefly through the persistent efforts of Dr. Leonhard Stejneger, of the United States National Museum in Washington, D. C. He literally followed in Steller's footsteps, searching records in the cities of Windsheim, Wittenburg, and Halle, Germany, and examining Russian archives wherever information about Steller might have been preserved. He even visited Bering Island and saw for himself the places described in Steller's original journals.

History owes a debt of gratitude also to Dr. Doris M. Cochran, who succeeded Dr. Stejneger as Curator of Reptiles and Amphibians at the National Museum and who carefully preserved his many notes and references.

One of the finest contributions to the history of the North was made by the American Geographical Society of New York when, in 1922 and 1925 respectively, it published translations of Bering's logbooks and Steller's journals. These describe the critical parts of the expedition in the words of the men who led it, men who endured one of the most historic voyages of all time.

ANN and MYRON SUTTON

Yosemite National Park,
California

YOUNG GEORG WILHELM

Y OU'VE done it again!"

"Sh-h-h!" The younger boy raised a finger. "Listen."

The older boy peered about in the dense forest.

"Georg Wilhelm," he said, impatiently, "you've gotten us lost again."

Without a word, Georg Wilhelm crept through the forest, trying to be quiet and to keep from breaking leaves or twigs beneath his feet.

A shock of red hair fell over his face, and with a puff he flipped it back. His Sunday coat was smudged, but who cared? Spring was here!

"Wait!" he said, stopping suddenly. "There! Do you hear it?"

The older boy listened again, then shook his head. "Not a thing."

"The hazel grouse, silly! You hear it only at this time of year."

"Hazel grouse? Is that why you brought me all the way in here?"

"No, no," Georg Wilhelm replied, with a twinkle in his eye, "I have something else to show you."

"What is it?" the older boy inquired.

"A surprise."

"What kind of surprise?"

Georg Wilhelm laughed. "Wait and see!"

"If you weren't my little brother, I'd . . ."

"Sh-h-h." Georg Wilhelm held his fingers to his lips. "You have to be quiet, Augustin."

With Augustin following, Georg Wilhelm tiptoed through the dark, mold-scented forest of towering beech trees. The trail led across a moor of heather and prickly gorse. At the edge of the moor they came to a huckleberry bush and stopped for a moment to pick berries.

"If we're lost," Augustin whispered, "at least we'll have something to eat!"

They went around a meadow where scarlet poppies were blooming. Georg Wilhelm stopped again. "We're closer now," he said.

They went back into the forest and soon came to a small stream that murmured faintly. High overhead some birds were chattering in the trees. Then from the distance came a whistling sound.

"That's it," Georg Wilhelm whispered. "That's the hazel grouse."

"I hear it now," said Augustin. "But I still want to know. What's your surprise?"

"Sh-h-h. It lives there beside the stream."

They heard a rustling of leaves.

"What is that?" Augustin asked.

Georg Wilhelm pointed. "Look—over there in the thicket."

Augustin followed the line of his younger brother's arm. In the shadows he saw a face with wide, staring eyes and long whiskers.

"A wildcat!" he shrieked. Instantly he was off at a run.

"Wait!" Georg Wilhelm shouted. "Wait! Come back!"

But Augustin was gone.

The wildcat leaped across the stream and disappeared into the woods on the opposite bank.

"Oh, Augustin!" Georg Wilhelm stamped his foot in a huff. He could hear his brother thrashing around in the woods in the direction from which they had come. "Very well, go on back. See if I care," he shouted. Then he sighed. "No, you'll only get lost if I don't show you the way home. Augustin! Wait! I'm coming!"

He took a shortcut and caught up with his brother. "Through here," he shouted, dashing into a clump of woods.

He led the way down a ravine and through a patch of tall trees at the bottom. They ran up over a fern-covered rise, straight across the meadow of scarlet poppies, and then along the edge of a marsh.

"We'll never find our way out," Augustin cried, puffing.

"Just follow me," Georg Wilhelm said.

Presently they heard shouts and ran out of the forest into an open meadow where people were picnicking beside a road.

"Come here this instant," Mama Steller said. She was holding a willow switch. "Shall I use this on you?"

Georg Wilhelm was breathless. "Mama! We saw a wildcat. The first one I have seen in Schlossbach Forest this year!"

"And it may be the last," Mama Steller said, folding her arms. "Your father and sisters and I have been calling you for an hour. You did not get permission to enter the forest . . ."

Augustin broke in. "Mama, it is my fault. We wandered away . . ."

Capercaillie bird

Mama Steller said: "Harrumph!" She always said that when she was angry. "Just because you are older than your brother, Augustin, you need not make excuses for him. I know perfectly well what happened. Georg Wilhelm, if you get lost in there again, you'll not be allowed to go to the celebrations."

"But Mama . . ."

"I mean it. No celebrations."

All that week Georg Wilhelm went directly home from school each day. He stayed well within the walls of Windsheim. He didn't dare to go near the city gates. He knew that Mama Steller had meant what she said.

And yet he also knew that the herons would be nesting. The capercaillie birds would be dancing. Somehow he had to get back to the forest.

He tried and tried to think of a way. Perhaps Papa Steller would let him go. He might ask: "Just for a little while?" But no, he knew that wouldn't work. Papa Steller always had the same reply: "Didn't you hear what Mama said?" And that would be that.

Maybe Augustin could help. But no, Augustin was too busy in high school.

Should he sneak out to the forest after school? Yes! He knew where a flock of partridges came to feed every day, late in the afternoon.

But then, on second thought, what if he got caught? And he *would* get caught. He was sure of that. Mama Steller always knew exactly where her children were.

Whatever happened, he must not miss the parade and festival in memory of Martin Luther. All Germany would be celebrating.

All right, then. He'd wait until after the celebration to go back to the woods. "Back to my animals," he said. "I'll see to it!"

Meanwhile, there was new excitement at school. Everybody was learning about the great religious leader Martin Luther. They learned how, a long time ago, Luther had become a monk. They learned how he had given up everything he owned, how he had gone without food, done hard work, humbled himself. While doing all this he had gradually realized that he could not agree with many of the beliefs of the church. Finally, he had written some papers saying that many reforms were needed. This led to the founding of a new branch of religion that came to be known as Lutheranism.

That had been in 1517. Now the year was 1717 and Georg Wilhelm was as excited as everyone else. In the two hundred years that had passed since Luther's "Reformation," many German cities had become Lutheran. Windsheim was one of them. That's why Windsheim was celebrating. That's why the pupils in school were learning all about Martin Luther.

Georg Wilhelm was eight years old and, with the

Windsheim

other boys in school, he was to march in the procession. He could hardly wait for the day to come. He'd never marched in a procession before.

So he behaved especially well. On Saturday he climbed up the winding streets of Windsheim to the church of St. Kilian. From there he looked down upon the ring of gardens around the old city. He tried not to look at Schlossbach Forest, out there beyond the city gates. He tried not to think of the hazel grouse calling, or of how much he wanted to see the wildcat again. Instead he looked down on the city square and saw the school.

He had entered school when he was five years old. Everyone started to learn Greek and Latin during the early years of school. The pupils also studied the writings of ancient philosophers.

Sometimes his lessons were very difficult, but Georg Wilhelm didn't mind that at all. "I like to study," he said. He took books home to read, and before long he had advanced to the head of the class. That made his father and mother very proud of him.

"You will make a very smart minister, my boy," said Papa Steller.

Georg Wilhelm smiled. "And not a cantor like you?"

"No, no. Oh, I'll admit that the life of a cantor is a good life. I sing and lead the choir, and I like it. Herr Bach, the great musician, is a cantor. So was George Friedrich Handel, many years ago, in England . . ."

"Then I'll be a cantor, too," Georg Wilhelm said. "I like to sing, and I can compose music. Do you want to see my latest composition?"

"Now, now, my boy," said Papa Steller, "I can see already that you will be a minister. A good one, too. And not a musician."

"Yes, Papa."

Secretly Georg Wilhelm knew what he wanted to be. It was not a minister. And it was not a cantor. Someday, somehow, he would become a naturalist. Then he could learn all about the wild plants and animals everywhere.

At last the day of celebration arrived. Georg Wilhelm and his brothers were dressed in their finest velvet coats and black trousers. As a treat, each was given a cube of candied citron to eat.

Georg Wilhelm saw people coming from miles around. He saw farmers from the fields and noblemen from the castles. It seemed as if everyone in Windsheim was there to follow the procession from the church to the school.

He watched the solemn members of the Inner and Outer City Councils take their places near the head of the procession. Then he saw the supreme judge, dressed in finery. Then the burgomaster, or mayor, of Windsheim, in his ceremonial robes. All the dignitaries of the church were there. Georg Wilhelm took his place with the pupils from the school who made up the final part of the procession.

After suitable prayers and benediction, the elegant company slowly proceeded to the school.

When everyone had assembled at the school, the rector delivered an oration about all the great things that Martin Luther had done. When he finished speaking, one of the students recited a poem. Then came more praises of Luther, and stories of his life were told. Finally there were prayers.

It was evening by the time everyone returned home. Georg Wilhelm had found the celebration so thrilling that when bedtime came he could not sleep. He would remember that day for a long time. And he wondered what Martin Luther must have thought, looking down from heaven.

Maybe Papa was right. Maybe he, Georg Wilhelm, would become a minister after all.

Yet as soon as he could get away again he slipped into Schlossbach Forest and crept down his favorite paths. He followed foxes and ran with the deer. He saw the wild-cat several more times, and watched it playing with other wildcats. Tingles went down his spine when he heard a wild boar in the distance. Sometimes he sat silently for hours watching badgers dig their burrows. And now and then, to his great delight, the largest bird in all Europe,

Wild boar

the great bustard, soared high above on wings eight feet in span.

The more he saw, the less he could keep his mind on music lessons and school work. From his teachers he learned languages and history and writing, but what did they know of the hazel grouse in the forest? What did they care how an otter spent the winter, how a flower opened, or how a bee gathered pollen for making honey?

When Augustin graduated and went away to study medicine, Georg Wilhelm felt lonely. But soon he entered high school himself. Then he was busier than ever. He had to put off many of his exploring trips.

The time was flying by. News came that Augustin was to be married. Ah, what an occasion! Augustin was making a success of himself. He graduated as a doctor from the University of Halle and received an appointment as a court physician in the little Duchy of Barby. There he'd fallen in love with a minister's daughter.

"Her name is Sophia," Augustin wrote, "and how very charming she is! You would love her."

Georg Wilhelm liked her even though he had never seen her. In fact, he wrote a poem for the occasion and composed a cantata to be sung at the wedding. If Augustin had not been so far away, Georg Wilhelm would have walked to the wedding.

"But, alas," he wrote in reply, "the professors would not let me come. We are very busy in school."

Georg Wilhelm and his classmates were studying the Bible and reading books by Ovid and Justinus and Aristotle. Next to the Bible he liked Aristotle best. That was because Aristotle had written many interesting things about animals.

And then one day another letter came from Augustin.

He was writing a book himself. "A very unusual book," he said. "You will want to read it. Mama says you are growing very tall for your age. Well, my book tells why people grow tall. I am going to dedicate it to the King."

That was so like Augustin. He dearly loved royalty.

But what he said was true. Georg Wilhelm was growing tall indeed. In Schlossbach Forest he now had to duck under branches that had not hindered him before. Just the same, he went into the forest whenever he got a chance —and he took with him anyone who would go along.

His three sisters—Elizabeth, Ann, and Maria—did not go into the forest, but when his two little brothers grew older he took them for walks.

"Michael! Gustav!" he would call to them. "Look. The potentillas are in bloom."

"What's the po— poten— po-ten-till . . .?"

"See this little yellow flower?"

"Yes."

"That's the potentilla. Do you know that it is in the same family of plants as the strawberry? You like strawberries, don't you?"

"Oh, yes! Yes! Let's hunt some."

And away they would go, jumping, and racing each

Potentilla

other through the woods. Georg Wilhelm had to run to keep up with them.

At length, after the fifteen years of school that was customary in those days, the time drew near for graduation. "I can hardly wait," he told his father one day. "I want to go places and learn things. I want to learn everything!"

"Wait a minute, my boy," Papa Steller said. "It is all right to be a little impatient. But you must learn to control your impatience."

"Yes, Papa, I know. But the world is so big!"

"You cannot learn everything. You must decide what you *will* learn."

At school, the rector made an announcement. "As you know," he said, solemnly, "we make available each year to some worthy student a scholarship that will pay his expenses to study religion at the University of Wittenberg."

Georg Wilhelm's heart leaped. Wittenberg! That was Martin Luther's town. The university was where Luther had taught.

"This year," the rector continued, "it is my privilege to award this scholarship to a graduating senior whose marks and attitude have been exemplary not only in the lower grades but in high school as well. This student has worked long and hard to achieve a position of great scholastic distinction. Therefore, on behalf of the city of Windsheim, I present this esteemed award to Master Georg Wilhelm Steller."

"Papa! Mama!" he shouted as he raced up the steps of their big home on the market square. "I've won it! I've won it!"

Mama Steller came from the kitchen drying her

hands on her apron. "You've won what?" she asked.

"The scholarship!"

Papa Steller came into the room. "What's this? What's this?"

"The scholarship, Papa. To Wittenberg. I've won it!"

Papa Steller shook his son's hand and said: "I'm proud of you, my boy."

"We all are," Mama Steller added. "Just think, Papa, our boy a minister."

Georg Wilhelm's shoulders drooped. "Minister?" he said to himself. He suddenly remembered the plants and animals of Schlossbach Forest. He remembered his plans to become a naturalist.

"Well," he thought, "now I'll *have* to become a minister." Then he put his tongue in his cheek. "At least for a while!"

On graduation day, September 12, 1729, he gave his farewell oration before a large audience including officials of the school, church dignitaries, his parents, brothers, sisters, classmates and their families.

He stood straight and tall, dressed in black trousers and white shirt. He spoke proudly, and in a clear voice.

"In physics," he said, "we see that the world around us reveals the power of Almighty God. Our great Luther proved that God is everywhere—in the air we breathe, in the sky that gives us rain, in the power of lightning and thunder. Today I speak of thunder. And, ladies and gentlemen, I shall prove to you that thunder is a witness and a vindicator of Divine Power . . ."

The audience sat entranced. Every eye was fixed upon him. Every ear caught his words. When at last he finished, it was with a poem he had composed. Then the graduation was over, and everyone came to congratulate him on his speech.

Two weeks later he said goodbye to his mother and father, and to his sisters and brothers.

"You will be home to us in two years," said Mama Steller with tears in her eyes. She grasped his arms and kissed him. "You will make such a fine minister."

He shook hands with his father.

"Goodbye, Father."

"Goodbye, my son. You will write to us."

And the boy was gone. As they watched him, waving their scarfs, dabbing at their eyes, they could hardly have realized that it was the last time they would ever see him. Little could they dream that he would go to the farthest ends of the earth, never to return.

⊰ 2 ⊱

THE UNKNOWN

COMING to Wittenberg for the first time, Georg Wilhelm felt like a pilgrim on hallowed ground. He went to the famous church where Luther had announced his reforms. Inside was Luther's tomb. Georg Wilhelm stood before it for a long time.

He wanted to visit the old monastery in which Luther had lived, but it was time to enroll at the university.

It was a bigger school than he had ever seen. Hundreds of boys were arriving from all over Germany. He went among them, introducing himself, asking where their homes were, trading stories, talking eagerly of the coming lessons. There was no one as concerned as he with natural science. But that was understandable. There were not many science classes here.

When classes began, Georg Wilhelm worked hard— attending lectures each day and studying by candlelight in his room at night. Often several of the boys would study together. Then they would talk. Sometimes they talked about the Bible. Sometimes they talked about their homes, or about the government. Almost always, Georg Wilhelm would hold them spellbound by telling of his adventures in Schlossbach Forest.

Before long, however, he began to see that the professors at the university were not like his teachers at Windsheim. For one thing, they didn't all take as great a personal interest in their students. For another, they dictated their lessons. This meant that Georg Wilhelm and his classmates had to write down everything they said verbatim—exactly as it was spoken.

"How dull that is," he told one of his classmates. "If we write only what they tell us, how can we learn to think for ourselves? All we do is copy, copy, copy."

He did what he was told, however, even though he longed to be out-of-doors exploring along the River Elbe.

That winter he studied the art of preaching, and visited churches in Wittenberg and nearby towns. He talked with all kinds of people—old and young, rich and poor, the sick and the lame, peasant farmers, soldiers, young women from the theater, artists. He listened, too. And by listening he learned what were the hopes and ambitions of the people; what their troubles were; how they needed help and how he with his sermons could inspire them.

Imagine him, with the coming of spring, as he strolled humming down the country lanes on his way to preaching assignments. Imagine how often he paused to watch a butterfly on a flower. Or hamsters digging chambers in their burrows. Or birds flying in the trees.

Word arrived from Augustin that Sophia had had a baby. This made Georg Wilhelm an uncle—for the first time. So excited was he that he decided to hike the distance to visit his brother.

"Georg Wilhelm, my boy," Augustin said, shaking his hand warmly. "We meet again, after all these years."

"Augustin, I've missed you."

"Well, I've missed your taking me on trips to Schloss-bach Forest. You always knew twice as much about the birds and animals as I did. And on the other hand I always thought you were completely lost. I thought we'd never get out alive."

They laughed. Georg Wilhelm said: "I was sure I'd lost you that day we saw the wildcat. Remember?"

"I do indeed," Augustin said, "and how many years ago it seems. But come, come. You must meet dear Sophia. You have never seen your sister-in-law."

She was as Georg Wilhelm had pictured her: charming, soft-mannered, with a warm and gracious smile. She was handsomely fair and had blue eyes.

"She is lovelier than your letters told us, Augustin," he said.

Sophia was holding the baby. "Your niece, Georg Wilhelm," she said, proudly. "You see, she has red hair. She looks like you, I think."

Georg Wilhelm blushed.

After dinner, Augustin asked: "Have I guessed right from your letters? Are you unhappy at Wittenberg?"

"Well . . ."

"I'm not surprised, knowing you as I do. Wittenberg is too slow, too strait-laced. You need something to stretch that mind of yours."

"What would you suggest?"

Augustin sat back in his chair, thoughtful for a moment. "Do you really want to be a minister?"

Georg Wilhelm didn't answer.

Augustin went on. "No, I can see it in your eyes. Some day you'll go away, far across the mountains. You're ambitious, Georg Wilhelm. And a little temperamental, I must confess. But we love you for it. You'll not be a minister. An explorer is what you've always been. I've known it all along."

"Well, then . . ."

"You must leave Wittenberg."

"Leave Wittenberg?"

"Yes."

"But I have a scholarship from Windsheim . . ."

"It can go to someone else."

"But where would I go?"

"To Halle, my old school. Where else, for someone like you? The university at Halle is an exciting place. People go there from all over the world. You would love it. Some of the Halle men are even going to Russia, for the great explorations. How does that sound to you?"

It was true. Georg Wilhelm had heard of Peter the Great's plans to explore and map the Russian frontier. Already expeditions were under way.

"Think about it," Augustin said.

Georg Wilhelm promised that he would.

Back at Wittenberg he began to spend more and more time in the botanical garden. That was a garden in which the flowers and shrubs had been arranged according to their scientific order. It was easier to learn their names and characteristics that way, as well as the plant families to which they belonged.

He also went to the anatomical theater, a place where lessons on the anatomy, or composition, of the human body were given. Eagerly he watched demonstrations made on cadavers—human bodies that had been contributed for the study of medicine. The professors injected the internal organs with wax. This made the body appear lifelike. Then they showed what the parts of the body were and told how to treat them when people became sick.

Georg Wilhelm listened, fascinated. It was his introduction to the science of medicine and surgery. Once he thought of changing to the study of medicine. But that was impossible. His scholarship was for the ministry. And besides, he still loved the outdoors best.

He continued hiking to nearby towns to preach. Each time he gave a sermon his voice rang clear and sharp. His eyes flashed. His dark red hair was tossed in anger when he spoke of sinners, or was scraped back smoothly when he pleaded for peace and goodness.

Mama Steller was right. He would have made an excellent minister.

Early in December 1730, a great fire destroyed the central part of the city of Windsheim. It burned to ashes the hospital, the church of St. Kilian, and the meeting-house, and came very close to the Steller home.

"How glad I am that you are all safe," Steller wrote his family. "But my heart is broken at the loss of so much of our beloved city."

Help flowed in from all over Germany, and the city began to rebuild. But the public funds of Windsheim were exhausted.

"Well," Georg Wilhelm told his classmates, "that finishes me here. My scholarship has ended."

"What will you do now, Georg Wilhelm?"

"I'm not sure."

"Will you go back to Windsheim?"

The thought of returning had never occurred to him.

"No," he said to himself, "I'm free now. Free to go where I please. Free to study what I wish."

And then he remembered Augustin's advice.

The city of Halle in Germany had a market square in the center of town, and an imposing medieval town hall. The city's landmark was its great church with two towers connected by a bridge. In exploring the town, Georg Wilhelm came upon a statue of Handel, the composer. Georg Wilhelm thought of his father. Handel was one of Papa Steller's favorite musicians.

But Halle was also famous for its university. And to Georg Wilhelm's great delight, there were many courses in natural science.

"Oh, yes," one of the students told him, "we've got everything here. Science, medicine, religion and—well, just everything. Are you enrolling?"

"I think so," Georg Wilhelm replied. "I have to find a job first. I don't have a scholarship any more."

"A job? Oh, that's easy!"

"Where?"

"At the children's school."

"The children's school? Where's that?"

"Right here at the university. It's a big place."

It was indeed. Nearly two thousand children came to it. There was a school for boys and a school for girls, a hospital, a pharmacy, a printing office, and a book store.

Georg Wilhelm had never been in such a big school before. He went to one of the head teachers.

"So you're looking for a job," the teacher said.

"Yes, sir."

"Well, what can you do?"

"I can teach, sir."

"What can you teach?"

"Religion, philosophy, music, language . . ."

"Language?"

"Yes, sir, Latin, German . . ."

"Well, well, well," the teacher said, scratching his head. "That's quite a list of abilities for a young man."

"Thank you, sir."

"How old are you?"

"Twenty-two, sir."

"All right, you're hired."

"Oh, thank you, sir, thank you."

"You'll be one of more than 160 teachers in this school. Many of them are, like you, earning their way through the university by working here. We'll expect you to conduct yourself properly at all times, in and out of class. Is that clear?"

"Yes, sir."

And so Georg Wilhelm began his double career at Halle, studying at the university and teaching at the children's school.

His meals were plain and simple—bread, meat, a few vegetables. His room was simple, too. But he didn't mind. In fact, he liked it that way. He had come here to learn, not to live in luxury.

He entered earnestly into the study of natural science. Here there were classes in botany and medicine. There were lectures in which the professors revealed the inner and outer structure of animals. There were classes where insects were dissected with the scalpel and examined through the microscope.

Month after month passed, and he hardly knew that the time was flying. Everywhere there were class discussions on science, or on religion, or on politics, and, as usual, he jumped right into the middle of them. And he almost always won his points.

"All right, Georg Wilhelm," his classmates would say, "you win! You always know the right argument."

"I can't even bluff him," said another.

"The trouble with Georg Wilhelm Steller," said another, "is that he is nearly always right. And he can prove it."

"The man's a genius!"

So rapidly did he prove himself that he started teaching a class in Latin to the pupils of the children's school, and before long was teaching a class in plant study at the university itself.

Whenever he could get away, alone or with classmates, he went on long excursions in the countryside. The Harz Mountains rose to the west, springing curiously and suddenly from the level land that surrounded them on every side. Georg Wilhelm crossed the flat plains from Halle and climbed into the mountains. He toured the tunnels and galleries of Stollberg mines, and hiked in the beautiful valley of Tyra.

And the more he saw of the world, the more he wanted to see the rest of it.

He read every book he could get his hands on. All over the world an age of discovery was in full progress. Everywhere expeditions were putting to sea and sailing into the unknown. He read of swashbuckling heroes like William Dampier, an English buccaneer and navigator who explored the South Seas and wrote about the world of nature that he saw.

Georg Wilhelm found a book by Jonathan Swift entitled *Gulliver's Travels into Several Remote Nations of the World,* and read it from cover to cover.

He got a copy of a new book that had been translated into German a few years before. It was by a man named

Daniel Defoe. The name of the book was *The Life and Strange Surprizing Adventures of Robinson Crusoe.*

"What a wonderful story," Georg Wilhelm said to one of his friends when he had finished reading it. "What fun that must be to land on a distant shore, to explore the country, to live off the land."

He started to read *Robinson Crusoe* again.

Augustin now lived in Köthen, a day's hike away, and Georg Wilhelm took every opportunity to visit there.

"I knew you would like Halle," Augustin said. "But before long your studies are going to be over. What are your plans?"

"Ah," Georg Wilhelm answered, "that is something I have been asking myself."

"And have you made up your mind?"

"Not yet. My classes go so well at the university, I mean the classes I teach, that perhaps . . . perhaps I'll become a professor."

Augustin's eyes opened wide. "A professor!" he said. "That means you would have to see the King."

"Yes. Only the King awards appointments as professor."

"But would you be satisfied as a professor?"

"Well . . ."

"Georg Wilhelm, have you forgotten the explorations that are going on all over the world? Have you forgotten about the Russian expeditions?"

"I have not," Georg Wilhelm replied. "Only last week two scientists from the University of Jena came by on their way to Russia. They talked to our classes. They said they were going to the Russian Academy of Sciences. They said they hoped to be able to join some of the expeditions going far into the interior of Russia. Perhaps they would

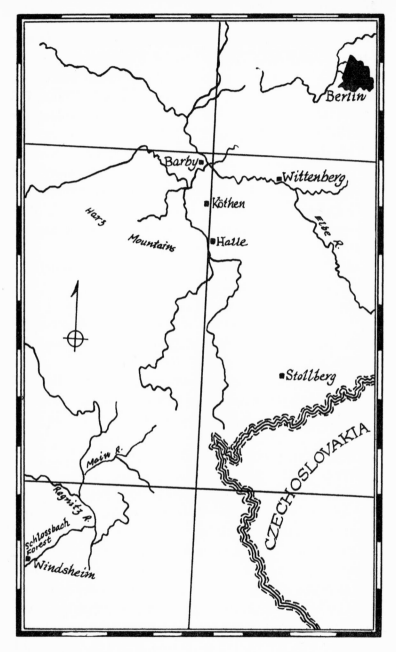

Germany: from Windsheim to Wittenberg, to Halle, to Berlin

get into Siberia, or even as far as the Pacific Ocean. Think of it, Augustin! Do you know how far the Pacific Ocean is from here?"

Augustin smiled. "It is just as I thought," he said. "You do not want to become a professor at all. I can see by the look in your eyes."

"Very well, then," Georg Wilhelm said. "But I have not yet found a way to go to Russia."

"You will," Augustin said. "If there's a way, you'll find it."

At last the time came for Georg Wilhelm to go to Berlin for a certificate of qualifications from the King. His professors told him that if he passed the examinations he could return to Halle as chairman of a department of botany. An exciting prospect! After all, he *did* like teaching university students. There were many places to explore about Halle. He could lead hikes into the forests of the Harz Mountains or into the valley of Tyra.

Yet, whenever he picked up his well-worn copy of *Robinson Crusoe,* the thirst for adventure came to him.

A few days before he left for Berlin, two German scientists came to Halle on their way to Russia. Eagerly Georg Wilhelm and his classmates sought them out.

"Why are you going to Russia?" he asked.

The scientists laughed. "Listen to that! He asks us why! Have you not heard? Do you not know that Russia is like a sleeping giant awakening? She is begging for scientists. The wages are good. There is even a chance of going on one of the expeditions toward Japan—or the Pacific Ocean! Think of it! You are all fools to stay here."

"And you, Steller," said another, "your fame as a botanist is rising all over Germany. We have heard of you. Yet you are young. Russia needs young scientists. Why not come with us?"

Georg Wilhelm frowned. "I am to receive a professorship here."

"Very well. If you wish to stay in one place all your life, and go to class day after day after day. Goodbye, gentlemen. May we meet again."

Georg Wilhelm found it very difficult to watch them depart.

On his way to Berlin he tried to forget what they had said, but couldn't. When he arrived in the great city and walked into the medical college for his examinations, he was wondering why he had not gone with them.

The examinations were easy. The examining commission informed him that he had made a very high score. "You will receive your certificate," they told him, "without any trouble. All you need now is an audience with His Majesty."

But as Georg Wilhelm was about to be received, the King fell ill.

A day passed, two, three, four. There was no word. The best doctors in Germany were called to the King's bedside, but the King did not recover.

Weeks passed, and the King did not improve enough to handle the affairs of the country. He could not even receive official visitors.

Georg Wilhelm waited. At any moment, he hoped, he would be summoned into the King's presence and be handed his certificate. He would then be a professor, and could return to Halle.

But the weeks went by and still there was no improvement.

"How long can I wait?" Georg Wilhelm wrote Augustin. "It begins to look as though I will lose my professorship simply because the King is too ill to give it to me."

The longer he waited the more impatient he became. He dreamed about Dampier exploring the South Seas. He stood with Crusoe, gazing at footprints on the beach, or with Gulliver among the Lilliputians.

In Berlin, there were, fortunately, other scientists, and Georg Wilhelm became fast friends with them. One day a friend said: "Georg Wilhelm, have you heard?"

"Heard what?"

"The news from Russia? Commander Bering is outfitting for another expedition to Siberia."

"Bering?" Instantly Georg Wilhelm was alert. "Where?"

"In St. Petersburg."

"When did you hear this?"

"This morning, by courier from Danzig. Isn't it odd? I can remember when Russia was a nation of barbarians. Now it is the most exciting country in the world. Look at all the explorations they have under way. Ah, how I wish I could go there."

Georg Wilhelm wasn't listening. "Tell me," he said, "where is the nearest unit of the Russian Army?"

"The Russian Army?"

"Yes."

"Why do you want to go to the Russian Army?"

"Why do you think? I want to join them."

"Georg Wilhelm, you are mad!"

"Mad?" Georg Wilhelm laughed. "I've been mad to stay here for weeks and weeks waiting for a professorship. If there's any expedition going to Siberia I'm going with it."

"But you can't. You don't even know how to speak Russian."

"I can learn, can't I?"

"But how will you get to Russia?"

"That's why I want to join the Russian Army!"

That night Steller left for Danzig, Germany, which was recovering from a siege by the Russian Army. The Russians, he learned, had organized their army only recently and now suffered from a lack of doctors. Georg Wilhelm knew he could easily qualify as a doctor. He would tell them that he had studied medicine and surgery at Wittenberg and Halle. He wouldn't need a certificate from the King, either.

So in Danzig he presented himself to the headquarters of Field Marshal De Lascy.

"Sir," he said, "I am a doctor. At your service."

The marshal smiled. "This is indeed a pleasure. Russia needs all the doctors she can get."

"I am ready."

"Very well. Our greatest need is in Poland at the moment. Our troops there must have medical help. You can leave on the next . . ."

"Sir," Georg Wilhelm interrupted, "I must tell you that what I really want is passage to St. Petersburg."

"Ah," the marshal replied, "it is just as well. We have troop ships carrying wounded across the Baltic Sea. We need doctors with them. It shall be as you wish."

For a while, Georg Wilhelm was attached to an artillery regiment in Danzig, caring for sick and wounded soldiers until they could be returned by sea to St. Petersburg. At length, as he had hoped, he was assigned to a transport carrying wounded soldiers to Russia.

"Tomorrow we leave," he wrote to Mama and Papa Steller, "and it has all happened so quickly that I'm not sure whether it is a dream. I know by now you must be disappointed that I did not return to Windsheim and become a minister as you had hoped. But these are things that God wills, and in His goodness He has opened for me the doors to my destiny in Russia.

"I cannot know what the future will bring. My greatest hope is to obtain a position at the Academy of Sciences in St. Petersburg, the capital of Russia. Some day I may get farther east, even to the frontier. May God will that, too."

It was autumn. Already icy gales blew down from the North, sweeping across the Baltic Sea. The troop ship tossed and rolled through the water, often bobbing helplessly near rocky shores.

In the Gulf of Finland a violent storm tore at her masts; suddenly the vessel rammed into a rock and stuck fast. Waves battered the sides and threatened to crumble the ship to pieces.

The soldiers became frightened. Those who could move tried to get into lifeboats.

"The end has come!" someone shouted.

"The ship is lost!" cried another.

"Help us! Help us!"

Then Steller shouted: "It's not lost yet. Back to your berths, you cowards. Ride out the storm like men, do you hear me?"

Crewmen and soldiers alike had been ready to climb aboard the lifeboats or leap into the sea. Now they paused. At that moment the gale changed direction; waves lifted the ship off the rock and blew it back into the open sea.

After a few more days, the weakened vessel arrived in Kronstadt, the port of St. Petersburg.

Winter snows were already falling as Georg Wilhelm turned east and headed inland toward St. Petersburg.

Suddenly he felt uneasy. What would he do when he got there? He did not even know how to speak the language of this strange country. He had no friends, no money, no job.

"Have I made a mistake?" The question haunted him over and over as he walked through the forests and marshes of the lowlands. "Have I made a mistake?"

❧ 3 ❧

ST. PETERSBURG

ON THE outskirts of St. Petersburg there was an Apothecary Garden. It lay on a small island separated from the city by a narrow arm of the Neva River.

Georg Wilhelm Steller pulled his jacket around his neck as he gazed down the river. It was November 1734. Through the leafless trees a cold wind swept down from the North. But he did not mind the cold. He was here at last!

He heard a voice behind him, speaking softly in Latin.

"You are pleased with the view?"

"Yes." Steller turned and saw, to his astonishment, an archbishop of the Russian church, a short man with kind eyes and a long gray beard. The archbishop wore a high, double-peaked hat, and around his shoulders was a white scarf.

"I come here often," he said. "It is one of my favorite places, even in winter."

"Yes," Steller said, "winter is an exciting time in the woods."

"You are a scientist?" the archbishop asked.

"I am, sir."

The archbishop smiled. "I thought so." He held out his hand to Steller. "My name is Theophan."

Steller bowed and introduced himself.

"Do you live far from here?" Theopan asked.

"To tell the truth," Steller replied, "I just arrived last evening. I came here to the garden hoping to find a botanist who might help me secure a place to live. I do not know how to speak Russian, save what little I learned from my patients in Danzig and on the ship. But I want to learn."

Theophan nodded. "And you want to enter the Academy of Sciences."

"How did you know that?" Steller asked.

The archbishop smiled. "All men of science who come here these days want to go to the Academy."

"Do you think I can?"

"We will see if we can arrange it. Now, as you have no place to stay, Herr Steller, would you do me the honor of coming to my house?"

Steller took the archbishop's hand and pressed it warmly. "Sire, I am your most humble and obedient servant. But I am also a Lutheran."

The archbishop smiled again. "We are not bigoted here," he said. "You will be welcome, whatever your faith."

"You cannot possibly imagine how happy I am!" Steller wrote Augustin that winter. "Theophan is the most respected churchman in all Russia. Mind you, it was he who delivered the famous oratory at the funeral of Peter the Great. He is a great man and is loved by everyone.

"Nor can I wish for a better home. The archbishop's palace is a lovely place. It is built among beautiful spruce woods and has enchanting views down the river. There are all kinds of boats at our disposal—even a yacht! And there is a summer house on the bay. What fun we shall have! How I wish all of you could be here.

"Many servants and church officials live here. Theophan has made me the household doctor and I am busy learning to speak Russian. But I like it. I am accepted by the Academy and this winter have been arranging the pressed plants stored in the herbarium. I can hardly wait until spring to go plant-collecting in the wild country around here."

When spring came, Steller was gone for days—neglecting his duties as doctor in Theophan's household. But as a result of his plant collections, he began to prove himself one of the most capable scientists in Russia.

The Academy, an imposing two-story structure that had once been a palace, had an astronomical observatory on top for studying the stars. There was a museum of natural objects inside. Steller was delighted. Night after night, the young Windsheimer pored over the collection of fishes, birds, mammals, and minerals.

Early in 1735, Archbishop Theophan told Steller that two Academy scientists were to be sent East. They would join the great explorer Vitus Bering, who was then in Siberia preparing for an expedition.

"Father," Steller exclaimed to Theophan, "it is my life-long wish."

"I know," the archbishop answered.

"Of course, I love it here, in your house. I wouldn't want to leave . . ."

"Nonsense, my son. There is nothing you want more than to go across Siberia, and I know it."

"Have they chosen who will go?"

"Not yet."

"Do you think there's a chance for me—I mean . . ."

Theophan raised his hand. "You must be patient. There are many here who are well qualified to go."

"Yes," Steller said, lowering his head, "but I will test myself against any of them. I will do whatever is necessary. I will study and read and . . ."

The archbishop said: "I shall see what I can do."

"Oh, thank you, Father! Thank you!"

"But you must work at it."

"I will!"

"You must learn all you can about the country. Do you know that it is nearly 7,000 miles to the peninsula of Kamchatka?"

"Yes, sir."

"That it might take you three years to get there?"

"Yes, sir."

"That you might have to travel alone most of the way, among barbarians and savages, and that you would be without supplies?"

"Yes, yes, Father. I know all that. I am even now learning the languages and dialects of the native tribes. I want to meet them."

"Then you must get hard to work. I cannot promise that you will be selected. But remember—the man best trained is best rewarded."

After a moment Steller said: "I must talk to people who have been there, people who know the country from experience. Do you know anyone who has been to Siberia?"

Theophan was thoughtful. "Yes, there is such a man, an old man like myself, who knows more about Siberia than anyone else."

"Where does he live?"

"That I do not know. I know only that he spent many years in Siberia and brought back much information."

"What is his name?"

"Messerschmidt."

Steller's eyes sparkled. "Of course! I've read his volumes in the library."

"Then you know of him?"

"Yes. But is he here? In St. Petersburg?"

"You must search for him, my son."

The search did not take long, not for Steller. He found Messerschmidt and his wife in a squalid hut in a very poor section of the city.

Mrs. Messerschmidt, a cheerful woman much younger than her husband, let him in.

"It is good you have come," she said. "We see few scientists any more."

There was a voice from another room. "Well? Well? Who is it?"

They found Messerschmidt seated in bed. There was a candle on a table beside him. The old man's face was wrinkled.

"You can't stay long," he said, coughing. "I am tired and do not want to talk."

Steller began to ask questions about Siberia. He wanted to know what animals the old man had seen, what plants, what minerals. He asked about the rivers and mountains, how cold it got in winter, how far it was to Kamchatka, the land at the east edge of Siberia, and what Kamchatka was like.

"No one knows what it is like," the old man said. "Few people have been there. A miserable place."

"I may be going there," Steller said.

"You may be what?"

"Going to Kamchatka, with Captain Bering's expedition."

Messerschmidt rose up in bed. "You fool!" he shouted. "Have I not told you enough? You do not know when you are well off. You must be out of your mind. Siberia is for criminals and exiles and heathen savages."

"But, sir . . ."

"No civilized person goes there now. Must I tell you about the natives out there? Must I tell of the barbarians who will assault you on the trail, of stupid government officials who harry you from morning to night, of storms and cold that freeze off your ears? Or of wild animals circling your camp at night so that you cannot sleep?"

"I know all that, sir."

"Then go back to your Academy. Stay away from Siberia. And from my house. I do not want to talk of it again. Get out! Get out!"

Mrs. Messerschmidt took Steller to the door and let him out, whispering: "Please do not be angry with him. He has been through very much."

"I'm grateful," Steller said. "I want more than ever to go now. He is a great man. Thank you."

"Goodbye," she whispered.

After that, he read and re-read every report that came from the East. Now and then it seemed that time stood still, that the decision on who would join Bering would never come.

He visited Messerschmidt again, but could see that the old explorer's health was fading. One night he arrived at the little hut to find a candle burning in the window. The old man had died.

For days he tried to locate Mrs. Messerschmidt—or Helen, as he now called her—and succeded finally in finding her at the home of a friend, in a well-kept part of the city.

"I'm sorry," he said.

"I have no tears," she replied. "He was a very sick man. Siberia was cruel to him. Too cruel."

"Is there anything I can do?"

"No," she said. "Thank you."

He started to leave, then turned and said: "Helen . . ."

"Yes?"

"We will go riding Saturday."

She looked surprised. "You are impetuous, Georg Wilhelm," she said, smiling, and went into the house.

By letter from Germany came word that Augustin and Sophia had had a new baby.

"How happy I am for you!" Steller wrote. "I would almost walk from here to Köthen to see you again."

He told about his work at the Academy, and how no one knew yet who would go to Siberia. He said that he was hoping at any moment to have good news to tell them.

"I am also anxious," he continued, "about Theophan. He is not well. I spend more and more time with him. I tell him that he is working too hard, but of course he does not listen. I am worried about him."

It was true. Theophan was growing slowly weaker. Steller had not noticed it at first. But now it was clear that the archbishop was seriously ill.

On July 28, 1736, the chief executive of the Academy summoned Steller to his office.

"Has His Excellency the archbishop improved?"

"No, sir."

"Ah, I am saddened. He grows weaker?"

"Yes, sir."

"God help him. It is a pity. Are you doing all you can for him?"

"I am, sir."

"You must. He is loved by everyone."

"I know, sir."

"Perhaps the news I have today will cheer him, and you as well."

"Yes, sir?"

"Please convey to the archbishop the information that you have been selected to serve as an adjunct of the Academy with the Great Northern Expedition."

Steller leaped from his chair. "Oh, yes, sir! Right away, sir!"

He dashed for the door and opened it, then caught himself and turned back. "Excuse me, sir. Thank you, thank you! From the bottom of my heart! Will that be all, sir?"

The executive smiled. "Isn't that enough?"

Theophan was very pleased when he heard the news. "I'm happy for you, my son," he said.

"And I, Father, am the happiest man in all the world!"

"There is much work ahead of you," Theophan warned. "The Chancellery must make the order official. The Senate must approve. You will have to examine all the official papers of the expedition. There are plans to make, supplies to arrange for . . ."

"I know, Father, but the decision has been made. I don't care now how long it takes. I'm going! That's what mattered. But . . ."

He paused. Theophan asked: "What is it, my son?"

"I cannot leave you, sire," Steller said. "You have done so much for me. I must stay here."

"I am an old man," the archbishop replied. "It is not I who will make Russia great. It is for you who grow now into manhood, who have the blood and the strength to bring us glory by your deeds. Do not delay for me, Georg Wilhelm, not a minute. Let God go with you to the ends of the earth . . ." He started to cough, and Steller withdrew.

He went at once to see Helen to tell her the good news.

"It's what you always wanted, isn't it?" she asked.

"Yes," he said, "but there is one thing more—to make it complete."

"What is that?"

"You."

"Me?"

"Yes, Helen. Will you go with me?"

There was a pause and he could sense that in her mind were passing all the tales that Messerschmidt had told about Siberia. She took his hand and said: "I'll let you know."

In five weeks Theophan was dead, and Georg Wilhelm, who had remained steadfastly at his bedside during the last days, was stricken with grief.

All Russia mourned. The highest dignitaries of the Holy Synod came, and last rites were performed with great ceremony at a monastery. Afterwards the archbishop was taken on a funeral barge to the city of Novgorod and entombed in the Cathedral of St. Sophia.

With his beloved friend and benefactor gone, Steller remained for a time in seclusion, going nowhere, seeing no one. After praying and meditating, he returned to the

Academy, saying to himself: "For Theophan I *must* make good. I must add to the glory of Russia."

He began to examine the maps and documents which had been sent back by Bering's and other expeditions.

His main task was to read the orders and letters from Bering's first expedition. That had been ten years ago. At that time the North Pacific Ocean was unknown. No one knew what lay north of Japan. Maps were blank north of California. Peter the Great's cossacks had pushed across Russia and conquered the peninsula of Kamchatka, which hangs like an icicle from the rim of Siberia. But beyond the edge of land—mystery.

Bering, by order of Peter the Great, had led an expedition along the Pacific Coast north to the Arctic Circle. That was enough to convince him that America and Asia were not joined together.

Month after month, Steller pored over the reports. By now he could speak and read the Russian language easily. He examined letters from members of the Admiralty. He studied Senate correspondence. Many high officials had not believed the results of Bering's first trip. This made Bering angry. He offered to turn right around and undertake a second expedition to show, once and for all, whether Russia and America were connected.

Bering's plans for a new expedition were overwhelmingly accepted. In fact, by the time the Senate and the Admiralty and the Academy had finished drawing up instructions, his suggestion had become a detailed plan for exploring and mapping nearly all the frontiers of Russia!

The Second Kamchatka Expedition, they called it. Or the Great Northern Expedition. There was to be a survey of northern and eastern Asia, including Japan. Astronomical positions were to be established in Siberia. Two ships were to be built on the far east coast and taken in search of America.

The more he read, the more excited Steller became. Over and over he read his instructions: "Likewise it is ordered that Steller shall be accepted for the Kamchatka Expedition as an adjunct in natural history . . . and devote himself . . . to natural history during the entire time the said expedition lasts, receiving a salary from the expedition in the sum of 660 rubles a year, plus quarters, firewood, and light."

The salary was nearly double that which most other scientists of the time received.

"It is amazing," he told Helen. "I can't believe it."

"Neither can I," she said.

"Helen, it is enough to keep us well, very well, even on the road to the Pacific. Won't you come with me?"

"As your wife?"

"How many times I've asked you!"

She took his hand. "All right," she said. "I have thought it over for many days. Life is lonely for me here, without—anyone. I will go with you."

"You will?" Steller could hardly believe it.

"I will," she replied.

The weeks and months passed quickly now. Steller ordered supplies and equipment and assembled them for the trip. He also had to select an artist. No explorer took to the field without a skilled artist to draw exact pictures of the plants, animals, and landscapes that were to be examined. This was long before the development of photography, so the only way to bring back accurate pictures of an expedition was to take an artist along.

Thus it was ordered that Ivan Decker, a dark-haired,

blue-eyed young Russian, who had recently served in the Engineer Corps, would accompany Steller across Siberia. With this, the preparations were nearly complete and the time for departure approached.

In a few weeks Helen and Georg Wilhelm were married. It was a quiet and simple Lutheran ceremony, attended by the high officials of the church.

"I am very contented now," Steller wrote in a letter to Augustin, "and am looking forward to the happiest days of my life. This is probably the last time you will hear from me for many months. I shall be in the wilderness from here to the Pacific Ocean, and may not get a chance to send you news. But you know that God is everywhere —and may He be with you, all of you, now and forever more."

On January 15, 1738, Steller and Helen left St. Petersburg in a troika, a sleigh drawn by three horses, and rode across the glistening snow through dense forest to Moscow. Behind them, Decker drove another troika, laden with supplies.

Moscow was the largest city in all Russia, and Steller's and Helen's eyes grew wide with wonder as they rode into it. They looked up with awe at the towers crowned by shining cupolas of gold and silver and gay colors. They rode in the circular streets around the Kremlin, a fortified palace where the Russian rulers had lived before moving to St. Petersburg.

What a thrill it was to be on the way at last!

Steller reported to the Siberian Office and made arrangements for mail, expenses, reports, and other matters that would be attended to while he was in the wilderness. Returning to the hotel where they had obtained a room, he found Helen standing beside her trunk and suitcases.

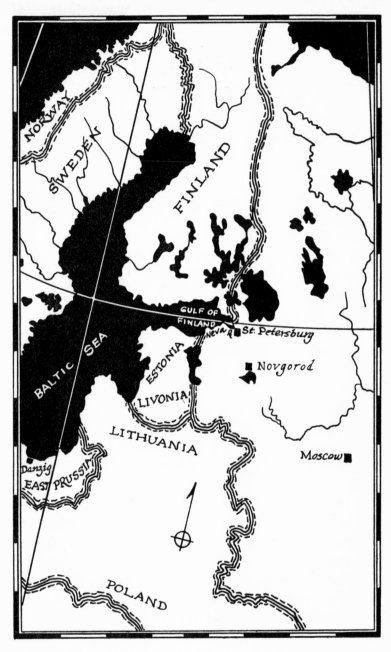

From Danzig, Germany to St. Petersburg and Moscow, Russia

"I'm going back," she said.

Steller was speechless. For a moment it seemed that he had neither seen nor heard correctly, or had misunderstood.

"You're what?" he whispered.

"I'm sorry. I have thought it over."

"You're going back? To St. Petersburg?"

"Yes. I know I will be useless to you in Siberia. I have heard what it is like. And it is better for me to go back from here."

"But your promises . . ."

"I thought I could go," she said. "I thought at least I could try. But now I know that I cannot bear to leave the comforts of civilization."

"You are my wife."

"And I am alive. St. Petersburg is alive. Moscow is alive. There are concerts, and parties, and theaters. I do not want to leave all those behind. You will be gone for years!"

The shock of surprise slowly left him. In its place came disappointment. "You have deceived me," he said.

On into the night they talked, and Steller tried every means he could to persuade her to go on. But all was in vain.

The next day, numb with disappointment, he arranged for her to stay a while in Moscow before returning to St. Petersburg. He made sure that she would be well provided for during his absence. Then, sadly, he took his leave.

There were tears in his eyes as he returned to Decker and the troikas.

"Hitch up!" he said, gathering strength and forcing himself to speak in a loud, clear voice. "Hitch up! We're off to Siberia!"

∞ 4 ∞

SIBERIA

For weeks they rode across the level steppes, or flatlands, of Russia. The powdered snow made troika travel easy. Or, changing to boats or rafts, they floated down mighty rivers, as had other explorers many years before.

They passed great marshes and deep, dark woods of pine and fir and silver birch. Now and then a squad of Russian soldiers, called cossacks, were met, or some native Tatar tribesmen, or a government courier.

Wherever he saw new plants and minerals, Steller stopped, scraped away the snow, and studied them. If they proved important, he preserved them carefully and packed them in one of the troikas.

Soon his sledges were heavily laden, and on arriving at the village of Kazan he placed his collections in boxes and sent them back to the Academy of Sciences.

The streets of Kazan were muddy with the spring thaw but Steller hardly noticed. He had become interested in the beautifully ornamented churches, the cathedral, and the monasteries. He wanted to stay, but knew he couldn't. The trip had only begun. There was no time to lose.

Beyond Kazan they left the Volga River and ascended the Kama, its chief tributary. Day after day Steller gathered new spring flowers that had burst into bloom. He carefully pressed each specimen he collected between sheets of paper and wrote down full information about it. He also wrote about the fishes, insects, snakes, and other animals that he saw.

Poor Decker! Constantly sketching, constantly drawing picture after picture, he was never able to keep up with his fast-moving master.

The days were so short! Or so it seemed to Steller. His work was never done by sunset; night seemed always to interrupt him. He read his books and wrote by firelight, and then in bed he looked up at the stars and thought about what he had found that day.

The more he traveled, the more his broken heart was mended. Only once did he mention his wife to Decker, and that was one night beside the campfire.

"I have forgotten her," he said. "I have forgotten her and fallen in love with Nature."

He had, indeed. He reduced his personal equipment so that he could collect and observe more intently. He cooked everything himself, putting soup, vegetables and meat into the same pot and boiling them together. Why not? That was the quick way. It gave an explorer more time to explore.

He ate in a single dish. He wore what clothes he could find or make. Any kind of boot or shoe suited him. "Think of the big caravans other men bring out here," he told Decker. "Not me. I want to see Nature as it is. I don't want to disturb it; if I do, it is no longer natural. I want to live with it. I want to see what happens and then try to understand why Nature does things the way it does."

When he was on the trail of a rare animal and could not stop to eat, he went hungry and thirsty a whole day.

But he found out new things that way—things nobody had ever known before. And in his notebook he wrote everything down with great care.

As they passed Ekaterinburg, gateway to Siberia, Steller breathed happily. The air was clear and dry, so unlike the damp climate in St. Petersburg. They were getting deeper into the unknown wilderness. When they arrived at the fortified city of Tobolsk, capital of Siberia, Steller hired a guide named Danilov, a rugged, black-bearded woodsman who knew the frontier well.

"How far are you going?" Danilov asked.

"To Kamchatka," Steller replied. "Can you take us there?"

"I take you to the moon, you pay right!"

"I'll pay right," Steller said. "How long will it take?"

Danilov spread his hands and shrugged. "Who knows? It is very, very far."

"How far?"

"Many thousand miles."

Steller reached into his coat and took out some money. "How about a hundred rubles?" he asked.

"Oh, Master," Danilov replied, eagerly, "for one hundred rubles it is not far at all! Come now. We go!"

They pushed off in a boat down the Irtysh River, and for hundreds of miles—down rivers, and up tributaries, and then overland—they traveled farther toward the East and the wild frontier.

The winter of 1738–39 was spent in Tomsk, a town surrounded by many farms. It was like other Siberian towns in that it had a palisaded fort, government buildings, churches, and log houses. There was a large wooden bazaar, or market place. Some of the storekeepers sold coats made of animal fur, and Steller soon knew why.

The temperature that winter plunged to forty-six degrees below zero!

At Christmas he came down with a fever so severe that Decker and Danilov feared for his life. They watched over him for days, just as he had doctored their ills and injuries on the trail. They nursed him slowly back to health.

But, as usual, he was impatient. In spite of his weakness from the fever, he ordered the sledge packed, and the little party set out across the glistening snow just after New Year's Day, 1739.

It took ten days to make the trip to Yeniseysk. Here Steller was overjoyed at meeting some naturalists who were on their way back to the Academy of Sciences after having explored farther east. He exchanged books and information with them, and even artists. Decker was assigned to return to St. Petersburg, and Steller took on a man named Berckhan, an artist his own age—just turning thirty.

Steller said goodbye to Decker and then, with Berckhan and Danilov, set out on the trail again, listening to the clop-clop of the horses' hoofs as the troikas were pulled across the snow. Everything was cold and barren, and there were few plants to collect, but for the moment Steller didn't care. On the horizon ahead, he could see lofty, snow-capped mountains, higher than any he had ever seen before.

It was early spring when they arrived in Irkutsk, capital of the Siberian province of the same name. While Danilov arranged for supplies, Steller hiked across the plains surrounding the town and studied the mountains in the distance. He hired a horse and rode through forests along the Angara River, stopping now and then to examine and collect fishes and crustaceans. His saddle bags were bulging when he rode back into town.

Irkutsk was in reality a palisaded square, open toward the river. Steller turned into town and rode past the wooden fort and the churches and monasteries. Later he visited the bazaars.

Not long after this, the people of Irkutsk discovered that he was a doctor. As soon as the word spread, they began to bring their troubles to him, for doctors were rare in this wild land. From then on, he had little time for fishes and flowers.

Danilov, meanwhile, was having trouble securing boats and supplies for the rest of the journey.

"Why? What is the trouble?" Steller asked.

"The Navy," Danilov replied.

"The Navy? What do you mean?"

"I go to the Chancellery," Danilov said. "The officials are nice to me. I ask for boats. They not so nice to me. I ask for food, supplies, medicine. They tell me go home!"

"But what does this have to do with the Navy?"

"I tell them who you are," Danilov explained, "and they say 'Herr Steller? Yes. We have his request.' I say all right, what they do about it? Where can I pick up boats? They say, 'Too late. No boats.' I say, where are they? They say, 'We give boats and supplies to naval officers.'"

"What naval officers?"

"The expedition, sire."

Steller frowned. "Well, there is not much we can do about that. The naval officers have to go ahead of us and build the ships for the expedition. We will keep trying. But, Danilov, we must not waste the summer."

"No, sire."

"Tell me, have you been in the Barguzin Mountains?"

"Oh yes, sire."

"We will go there at once. Berckhan and I have explored the forests around Irkutsk and are through here. Can you get boats to take us across Lake Baykal?"

"Yes, it is not far; we only borrow boats for that. When you leave?"

"When can you be ready?"

They crossed the wide expanse of Lake Baykal, one of the largest lakes in the world. Strong winds blew across the open water, and more than once threatened to upset the boat. Following the west side of the lake, they stopped intermittently along the shore to search for new kinds of plants and animals.

Finally, on reaching Barguzin Bay, they rowed up the Barguzin River for nearly twenty miles and went ashore to set up summer headquarters at a fort in the wilderness.

The land around them was like a strange, new world. Steller had seen nothing like it before. Here was Schlossbach Forest and Halle and Russia all rolled into one— only bigger! He felt like Robinson Crusoe. He knew that he was the first naturalist to explore this region. If Augustin could see him now! And Theophan!

Mountains towered above him in the cold, blue sky. Their lofty summits were jagged and snow-capped. Looking up, he knew that, before anything else, he must climb them.

The next day he did. It was a long climb, and a difficult one. But after all his explorations and hikes and animal hunts, he had become very strong. The air was fresh and pure. Climbing for long hours only made him more eager to get to the top.

When he reached the summit and looked around, seeing the mountains and plains and forests of Siberia stretching in all directions, his heart was filled with joy. "The view overwhelmed me," he wrote in his diary later. "On these snow-covered cliffs I found dwarf cedars, dwarf birches, elders, and little willows creeping along the mountain top like garlands on the head of an old man. I felt myself stimulated by the pure air and the very strangeness of the place. It seemed as if I was in a wonderful dream or under a magic spell."

All summer he explored the Barguzin Mountains, writing hundreds of pages of notes and records. He discovered many plants new to science, including a magnificent rhododendron with a yellow flower. Its leaves were highly poisonous, which was not discovered until a pet deer at the fort ate several of them.

Danilov shouted: "Look at that deer!"

The animal jumped back and staggered, jerking its head from side to side. It fell on its knees and tried in vain to rise. Steller gave it a little milk, but for nearly four

Yellow-flowered rhododendron from Barguzin Mountains

hours it lay in a stupor and then was shaken by convulsions. They were afraid it would not survive. But presently it recovered and pranced about as lively as ever.

When autumn came, Steller and his little party returned to Irkutsk, laden with collections of animal skins, plants, insects, and minerals.

They still could not proceed to Kamchatka, for the boats and equipment were not yet ready. Steller and Berckhan then set to work preparing a report on the natural history of Irkutsk, and for months were busy writing, drawing, and studying.

One day Steller asked Berckhan: "How much paper have we left?"

"Not much, sire."

"Then let us get some."

"But the nearest place is on the Mongolian border! They say it is 333 miles there and back."

"Then let's be off!"

"Now? In the middle of winter?"

"We need paper, don't we? For notes, for drawings, for pressing plants?"

"Yes, but . . ."

"Then hitch up the sledges!"

And so in the middle of winter they traveled through the icy cold to the trading center of Kyakhta and obtained the paper they needed. While there, they joined in the celebrations for the Chinese New Year. The masks, street processions, and weird oriental music made Steller even more aware that he was in a strange and remote land.

By the time they returned to Irkutsk, Steller's patience at the delays in travel began to grow thin.

"We have been here long enough," he said. "Why can we not get boats and equipment?"

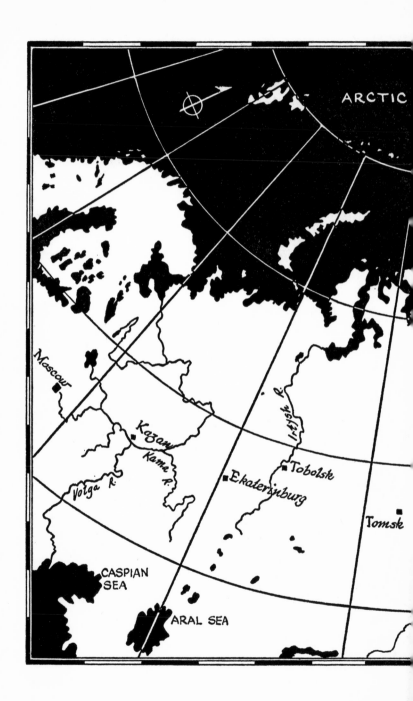

Steller's trip across Russia—from Moscow to Okhotsk

Danilov shrugged. "The officials not say. They not got boats. So what we do?"

"How about sledges?"

"Plenty sledges."

"Well, it is still winter. Tell them we do not need boats."

"But when we get to the Lena River, sire, we must have boats."

"We'll worry about that when we get there. The expedition will be waiting for us in Kamchatka, and we cannot delay any longer. If we need boats we'll make them ourselves."

Thus early in 1740 they set out on the road that led along the south end of Lake Baykal. Weeks later they arrived at Fort Kirensk, where Steller decided to wait for the ice to break up on the River Lena. While waiting, he hired carpenters to build boats. Finally, in May, they pushed off on the thousand-mile trip down the river to Yakutsk.

Now and then they passed bands of native tribesmen who stood at the edge of the river, watching. Frequently, Steller ordered the boats ashore so that he could talk with the natives. Or he invited them to his campfire at night, and conversed in the native languages that he had learned at the Academy. Each time, after they had gone, he got out his note paper and recorded the details of what he had seen and what the tribesmen had told him.

When the party arrived in Yakutsk, everything around them had become primitive—in comparison with other towns they had passed through. As they rode into the village, Steller saw that the huts and dwellings were crudely constructed.

"Now we are really on the far side of Siberia," he said
to Danilov. "This is the frontier."

They stayed in Yakutsk long enough to rearrange their
equipment and collections and make preparations for the
final lap of the journey—overland to the Sea of Okhotsk.

They arrived at last at the seaport of Okhotsk, a newly
built village. They saw at once what a busy place it was.
Preparations for the expedition were being made. Down
in the bay two ships, the *St. Peter* and *St. Paul,* were
under construction. These were the ships that would carry
the expedition out into the Pacific Ocean. Logs, timbers,
nails, and food were being brought in from everywhere,
and men of many nationalities scurried hither and yon.

Steller went immediately to the expedition headquarters and announced his arrival. A naval officer then con-
ducted him through the muddy streets to report to Captain-Commander Bering. The barracks and headquarters
of the expedition were all new buildings, made of rough
logs that had been cut from the forest nearby.

As he was taken into Bering's presence he felt a kind
of awe. For years he had known the great Danish explorer by reputation only. He had read of Bering's ex-
ploits and voyages. He had read the official reports and
letters. It seemed as if he had known the old man forever. Yet somehow he had not expected to meet a man
whose hair was so gray, whose face was so lined and
drawn with age.

Bering's cold steel eyes sparkled when he greeted his
guest: "So you are Georg Wilhelm Steller," he said. "Sit
down. We have been looking forward to the arrival of an
adjunct of the Academy."

"Thank you, sir," Steller replied. "And I have been

looking toward this moment for many years. I am greatly honored to be here."

Bering leaned back in his chair and smiled—a warm, friendly smile. "It is kind of you to say that," he said. "How was your journey?"

Steller described his travels by sledge across the frozen plains, his boat trips on the rivers, his side trips to the Barguzin Mountains and the Mongolian border, and his studies and collections everywhere in natural science.

Bering said: "It was much work for you."

"Not at all," Steller replied. "What is work to others is pleasure to me. I am not happy unless I am busy."

Bering stroked his flowing silver beard. "Are you aware," he asked, "of the work ahead of you?"

Steller's eyes sparkled. "Sir, I have been hoping and praying for this task for a long time. I think even from the time I was a little boy."

"This is not child's play, my son."

"I am no longer a child."

Bering opened a journal on his desk. "I see here that you have many qualifications. The report from the Academy says you are a botanist. Is that true?"

"Yes, sir."

"And it says you are a mineralogist; can you tell the names of rocks and minerals?"

"I can, sir."

"And it says further that you are a surgeon—a doctor, that you are familiar with medicines and with methods of treating the sick. Is this also true?"

"It is."

"And you are a minister?"

"I have preached some and studied theology."

Bering leaned back in his chair again. A smile crossed his face. "Then let me say that *we* are happy to have *you* here."

"Thank you, sir."

"Now, as we already have a surgeon with the expedition, I shall list you officially as a mineralogist. Does that suit you?"

"Yes, sir. Perfectly."

"But understand that you may be called upon to use all your talents. Like the other members of this expedition, you are required to help promote, in every way possible, the glory of Russia."

"I am already dedicated to that, sir."

"Very well, then. Lieutenant Waxel is the first officer in charge. Report to him for assignment of quarters and arrangements of your servants and supplies."

"Thank you, sir," Steller said, rising. "May I ask when we will leave?"

Bering sighed. "Ah, there have been so many delays. We cannot say."

"Perhaps I will have a little time to explore around Okhotsk?"

"Perhaps. But do not remain away long."

"I won't sir. You can depend on that!"

Bering rose from the desk and went with him to the door. "You are anxious to depart?" he asked.

"I am."

"Well, I can say that it won't be long. We will leave soon for Avatcha Bay, on the far side of Kamchatka."

"That's on the Pacific Ocean," Steller said.

"Yes," Bering said, smiling. "It is where our voyage begins."

⤫ 5 ⤭

AVATCHA BAY

AT EXACTLY four o'clock on the morning of May 29, 1741
a shot rang out and broke the stillness of the sleeping
village on Avatcha Bay.

Steller leaped from beneath his bearskin robe and
stepped outside. It was still dark, though a faint light
shaded the eastern sky. He blinked and rubbed his eyes,
trying for a moment to remember where he was. He
could recall saying goodbye to Berckhan and Danilov. He
remembered the trip across the Sea of Okhotsk. Now, here
he was in Kamchatka. To the northwest lay Vilyuchensk
volcano, glowing dimly red in the blackness. Overhead,
like icicles piercing the Arctic night, hung many glittering
stars.

"The fog has cleared," he said, almost in a whisper.

The crisp cold stung his nostrils. He could smell the
thrilling tang of salt air flowing in from the Pacific Ocean.
Where else in all Russia, he asked himself, could such a
breeze blow? Where but at the high edge of the sea?

For a moment he stood motionless. One by one, candles brightened the tiny windows of the cabins and sod
huts in the village below, at the bay's edge, and lights
flickered in the warehouses and the barracks. Out in the

68

bay the *St. Peter* and *St. Paul,* their masts and rigging silhouetted against the dawn, lay at anchor with sails furled.

Steller hurried back to his room and lighted an oil lantern. Rough-hewn logs formed the walls of the room, which was empty save for the bearskin pallet on which he had slept, and a black leather bag suspended from a peg in one corner. He dressed quickly, pulled a canvas shirt over his shoulders, and drew the rawhide thongs about his neck.

"Master," came a voice from the door.

"Yes, Thomas?"

"You have heard the signal?"

"I have, and I shall be ready in a moment."

Steller laced his boots, which he himself had made from sealskin. "Have you seen Eselberg?" he asked.

"No, Master."

"Or Plenisner?"

"They slept on the ship. They are coming ashore now."

Steller placed on his head a weathered black sheepskin hat and tucked away the strands of reddish hair that fell over his ears and into his eyes. Then he slipped into a worn leather tunic, took down the leather bag, and went outside.

Grandly waving an arm toward the ships and the bay he said: "The fog has cleared, Thomas. This is the day!"

Thomas the Hunter grinned, the dark line of his mouth widening across a strong, square jaw. "Yes, Master," he said, his black eyes glowing in the light of the lantern he held up before them, "fair weather it is!"

Thomas was short—barely five feet tall—but Steller knew there was not a mightier hunter in all Kamchatka. His marksmanship was unsurpassed. And his endurance,

even in the severest blizzards, was equaled only by
Steller's.

Down in the village all was astir. From every window
an orange glow pierced the blackness. From every hut
and cabin came the sound of preparations. The longboats
had begun to arrive at the wharf. Steller thought he saw
and heard the artist Plenisner amid the cluster of lanterns
there. Plenisner's laugh was unmistakable. It could be
heard for long distances.

Dogs barked and yipped. Children shouted. Villagers,
shielding candles or carrying lanterns, moved across a
muddy patchwork of rock and sand and earth. They filed
past piles of soggy sailcloth and rusted cables. They
stepped over wooden blocks and walked past planks and
chains and nail kegs, toward the church on the hill.

Steller handed his leather bag to Thomas, saying:
"See that this goes aboard the longboat."

"Yes, sir. After the prayers I will meet you on the *St.
Peter.*"

On his way to the church, Steller heard a lusty shout.
"Ahoy!"

It was Plenisner.

"Ahoy and good morning, Herr Steller!" Plenisner used
the German title "Herr," for he was also German and,
like Steller, many miles from his native land. "A fine
day, is it not? Today we are sailors!"

"Aye, Friedrich," Steller replied, "but not really."

"Well, I feel like it. Today I think I have salt water in
my veins."

Plenisner laughed, a youthful laugh. He was Steller's
age, blue-eyed, full-bearded. He was a top-flight artist
and surveyor. Steller was elated that he had joined the
expedition. Assuredly there would be strange wild plants

and animals to be sketched as part of the scientific reports of the voyage. The artist's voice broke into Steller's thoughts. "Come, let us have this service over and be out to sea. By night we may be many leagues from here."

Steller caught his arm. "Avast! Where is our friend the navigator?"

Plenisner turned toward the wharf. "Eselberg? He was behind me, fairly on my coat tail. Why?"

"He owes me a wager. I talked with him last night, you know . . ."

"Yes, yes, yes, I do know!" Plenisner interrupted, laughing again. "You want to show him the way to America. You scientists are all alike."

"And why not?" Steller asked.

"Well, Eselberg's got his own ideas. After all, he *is* the ship's navigator."

"But it's all a matter of common sense. If we follow the 52nd parallel . . ."

"Now see here, my friend, the captain will abide by his own pretty ship's council; that's how we'll get to America. You know it. Eselberg knows it. The captain knows it."

Steller clapped him on the shoulder and turned toward the church, where the villagers were assembling. "Friedrich," he said, "you are impossible."

After the services, Bering sent for Steller. There was a worried look on the old captain's face.

"Dr. Feige is ill," he said.

"Dr. Feige?" Steller was surprised. "The ship's physician?"

"Yes."

"Is it serious? Perhaps he will feel better when we set sail."

"I'm afraid he will not be going."

"What?"

"He has notified me that he is too ill to undertake the voyage and has requested to be sent back to St. Petersburg."

"But, Captain . . . An expedition as important as this . . . We must have a physician."

"That is why I sent for you."

"What about Betge, the assistant surgeon?"

"He will be helpful," Bering replied, "but he does not have the knowledge of medicine that you possess. My request is simple. Will you assume the duty of ship's surgeon, with Betge as your assistant?"

"In addition to my duties as mineralogist?"

"Yes."

Steller paused. Below in the bay, the rowboats were being loaded. He could hear the eager voices of the sailors and see the flickering lights of the lanterns at the wharf. Then he turned to Bering and said, "You do me an honor, sir. I cannot refuse."

Gleaming sunlight spilled across the bay as the *St. Peter,* her sails taut in the breeze, moved like a silver cloud across the water.* How majestic she was! Aloft she carried all sails except the spritsail, and a powerful wind slipped over the water and through the rigging, puffing the sails and pushing her to the southeast.

Steller could not believe that all his dreams had come true! He had not even dared to wish for this much, even when at Halle he had read books about travel and exploration, and had talked with the scientists who had been on

---

*This was June 4th. The ships rode at anchor just outside of the harbor, for six days, awaiting favorable winds.

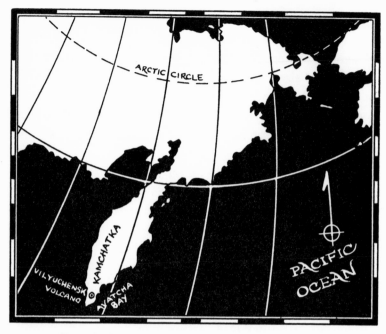

Kamchatka, the starting point of the expedition

their way to Russia. Augustin had been right. So had
Theophan. They had predicted this for him. They had
encouraged him. Now he was doing what few naturalists
ever got to do in an entire lifetime. He was sailing into
an unknown sea!

The *St. Paul* rode not far behind. Bells clanged on both
ships and Steller heard the mate's voice: "All's well.
Steady on course."

Both of the ships were two-masted, brig-rigged packet
boats, built to Captain Bering's specifications. Each was
eighty feet long and twenty-two feet abeam.

The *St. Peter* carried fourteen guns. Her decks and
hold were stacked with cargo, including salt, flour, and
hardtack enough to last for months. There were nearly

eight thousand pounds of groats (a dried grain used as a cereal). There were fifteen barrels of beef, eight of pork, eleven of butter, and more than a hundred water casks of different sizes.

Altogether it was a heavy cargo and under it the ship rode deep in the water, every block and every timber straining in protest as she surged through the dark blue sea.

"Lay out on the yards there, Mister!" the lieutenant shouted. "And sing out! All hands on deck!"

Steller, looking down from the quarterdeck behind the lieutenant saw the men scramble on deck and gather before him.

They were a strange lot. Some were young and some were old. Some were gunners and gunners' mates. Some were coopers and carpenters. Some were soldiers and grenadiers, trumpeters and servants. There was a cadet from a Yakut regiment, and there were cossacks from Siberia—silent, burly types. There was a blacksmith, a sailmaker, and a calker. There were hunters, interpreters, boatswains, men with good Russian names like Sorokin and Tchetnev, Semenov and Kukushkin. And men from other lands, including Germans like Steller and Plenisner. And there were some whose professions and names have faded with history. Counting the officers and crew, they totaled seventy-eight.

"Pay mind to what I say, ye lubbers," Lieutenant Waxel said, standing straight as a ramrod, "for I tell it to ye once, and henceforward ye'll know the law and abide by it. Hear me!"

The lieutenant's face was nearly hidden beneath the visor of the cap which was, as usual, pulled over his eyes. He had a square jaw, which added to the sternness of his bearing. He wore thick woolen trousers, grayish black, and these were neatly tucked into well-greased knee boots.

"This expedition," he said in a deep voice, "is for the benefit and the glory of Russia. By order of Her Imperial Highness Anna Ivanovna, we are bound for the continent of America."

Shouts burst from the lips of the men on the deck. It was not that they hadn't known. All had signed on (or been forced on) with the idea of going to America. They were just happy to be a-sea at last.

But Lieutenant Waxel did not smile. "By order of Captain-Commander Bering you are to know and obey the rules of the voyage. Now hear me! Captain Chirikov commands the *St. Paul*. The two ships are to stand close

The *St. Peter* and the *St. Paul*

to each other throughout, so that if one needs help, the other will be at hand. We are to keep together, work together, and do all in our power to advance naval science."

Steller saw the *St. Paul* following like a giant white swan. Both ships now approached the mouth of the bay. Steep mountain slopes, clad in green birch woods and luxuriant new grass, dropped to the water's edge. The vessels would soon be clearing the narrow passage that opened to the sea.

"We are to find out if Siberia and America are connected," Waxel went on. "We have heard of a great land to the east, where many trees grow, where natives wear walrus teeth in their lips, and where we may find many sables, beavers, otters, and wild deer."

Steller's heart leaped at the thought of it. What a wonderful land it must be!

"If on the way we meet a European ship, or any ship, we will learn the name of the nearest coast, make a landing, draw maps, and return to Kamchatka. We may be back in a month. Or we may be gone all summer."

Waxel paused. "Now hear this. Our instructions call for us to treat kindly any people we may find in this new land. We are to give them presents, and not harm them in any way. Is that clearly understood?"

The men nodded and murmured assent.

"Then do not forget it! We are to ask the natives the extent of their country and what they have, and they will be invited to become our subjects and to pay tribute. But —" and here he measured his words carefully— "if they are unwilling to do so, they are to be let alone. Hear ye?"

Murmurs again.

"No time is to be wasted in arguing with them. These are orders from the Imperial Senate and the Admiralty.

Our physician and mineralogist, Adjunct Steller, is to search for precious minerals. We look for rivers and harbors, and timber for shipbuilding, but these must be kept secret."

Steller saw the men glancing at each other in anticipation. But the officers seemed little moved. Eselberg, next to Steller, displayed no expression whatever. The gray-haired old navigator had served on many voyages. This was probably just another one to him.

Yushin, the second mate, stood behind Waxel, with his feet apart and his hands behind him. Yushin, keeper of the ship's log. How pompous he seemed! His long frock coat reached well below the knees. He wore an astrakhan hat, which made him seem officious, even superior. But his tender skin and paleness gave him away. A soft man, Yushin!

Steller's gaze shifted to the bulwarks, where Fleet Master Khitrov stood. Khitrov would have won no prize for neatness. He wore a fur cap, a torn deerhide jacket, and heavy canvas trousers tucked into knee boots made of cowhide and coated with tar.

Not an inspiring sight, Steller thought.

"This expedition," Waxel was saying, "may be more difficult and longer than any that has ever preceded it. For that reason, we may expect, upon our return, to be rewarded richly by Her Imperial Highness." He paused again. "Are ye with us?"

An immense shout went up from the men, and some threw their hats in the air. Still unsmiling, Waxel turned and went into his cabin, with Khitrov and Yushin following. Steller turned to Eselberg.

"My friend," he said, "if I find a gold mine in America I shall give it to you as a present from Her Imperial Highness, in reward for long and meritorious service in the Russian Navy!"

Eselberg laughed and turned away. "Ach! What would I do with a gold mine?"

Steller indicated the sails. "The wind is good!"

"Yah, yah," Eselberg replied. "Today it is. But who knows what gives tomorrow?"

"Then we will forget tomorrow," Steller said, laughing.

Plenisner was gleeful. "Hurrah!" he cried. "We're off, I think. Come, I want to show you something."

He pulled Steller up to the forecastle and stretched his arm toward the west. "There!" he said. "Do you see it? There goes Vaua Lighthouse!"

"The last point of land," Steller said.

"Yes, yes," the artist exclaimed. "Ah, Vaua, symbol of a vanishing land! We'll not see thy light again till summer's wane or winter's woe. Listen to me; why did I not remain a poet in St. Petersburg? What a happy life I would have led!" Then he was thoughtful for a moment. "No. It would not have been the excitement this one is. Look! Yonder, across the coast. The volcanoes of Kamchatka bid us goodbye!"

"Aye," Steller said, "it is a beautiful land."

"We go to a greater land, do we not?"

"Who knows?"

"Let us hope we find her, and soon."

"When shall we be there?"

"A few days," Steller replied. "A week at the most. We will not know until we find De Gama Land. In fact, we may not even find De Gama Land at all. It may not even exist."

A perplexed look crossed Plenisner's face. "What," he asked, "is De Gama Land?"

৫ 6 ৯

THE PACIFIC

THE DAYS passed by, and the winds freshened, filling the topsails and the lower sails and the staysails and the jib; and day after day the *St. Peter* and the *St. Paul* sliced the sea southeastward—across the unknown Pacific.

Georg Wilhelm Steller took his place in the captain's cabin. Thomas had placed his black leather bag there, as well as a sea-chest and the hides that served as blankets.

The cabin was small, little more than ten feet square. It had windows aft that looked out upon the sea and the wake of the ship; beneath them was a window shelf, or sitting place. Built-in bunks stretched along each side, with a sea-chest at one end.

On Bering's side, in one corner, was a desk on which were an oil lamp, a row of log books, and some maps. Above the desk a small bookshelf had been mounted, and this contained navigational instruments as well as worn, leatherbound books.

Overhead a lantern swung from the huge rough-hewn beams that formed the ceiling of the cabin. On Steller's side of the room was a vertical compartment that contained maps and charts, and on top of this was a platform on which a small oil stove had been mounted. Next to this, and in the corner, was a narrow partition that closed off the washroom.

It was hardly a luxurious compartment, compared with standards in St. Petersburg, or in Moscow, and it was small and crowded. But it was workable and compact, and space was at a premium on an expedition. Steller was perfectly satisfied. Vaua and the volcanoes of Kamchatka had dropped astern, and the expedition was on its way to America at last. What else could he want? He would have been glad to sleep on the yardarms!

The second day out, he decided that if he were going to examine closely the wildlife of the sea, he must have a convenient place on deck from which to observe and take notes.

"The forecastle," Plenisner said. "Where better?"

With the artist gaily helping, and with the ship's carpenter providing materials, Steller constructed a pair of crude seats. He also fashioned a railing to which they could cling in stormy, turbulent weather, and a shield behind which they could crouch on bad days to draw or to make entries in the journal.

That done, Steller brought from his sea-chest an old deer hide that he had used to throw over many a sled in the Siberian wilderness, and lashed it to the seats.

"There, now," Plenisner observed, "you'll not find as comfortable a seat if you sail the seven seas to Judgment Day."

Steller shook a finger at him. "Take care, comrade. This is not a lovers' seat nor a trundle bed. Make sure you have pen and brush when you sit here, for this is to be a busy place."

"What shall we call it?"

"Well . . . let's see . . . the Lookout. That's a simple name, isn't it?"

Plenisner agreed. "So be it. Now sit there and tell me about De Gama Land, as you promised."

Steller sat down. "Very well," he said, "but it is not a long story."

"Good. I like short ones."

"It is only this: A Spanish explorer named Don Juan de Gama sailed from China to New Spain many years ago and reported that he had seen the coast of a strange new land east of Japan. None of the land was explored and no one could tell whether it was an island or a whole continent."

"Was it America?"

"They didn't know. But there were maps. Sailors of the Dutch East India Company saw the land also. For that reason we sometimes call it Company Land. Others call it 'Yezo.' On some charts it is shown as an island separated by a strait from the Asiatic mainland."

"Well, then, there can't be much doubt about it."

"Perhaps. I have a map in my sea-chest, a map drawn by Joseph Nicolas DeLisle. You will remember that he was at the Academy of Sciences."

"The French geographer?"

"Yes. He said that De Gama Land must belong to a great continent connected with America."

"Then that proves it!"

"Ah, no, DeLisle himself has never seen it."

"But you, Herr Steller. Do you think it is there?"

Steller turned his head and smiled. "Friedrich, you forget. I am a scientist. I do not speak until there is evidence."

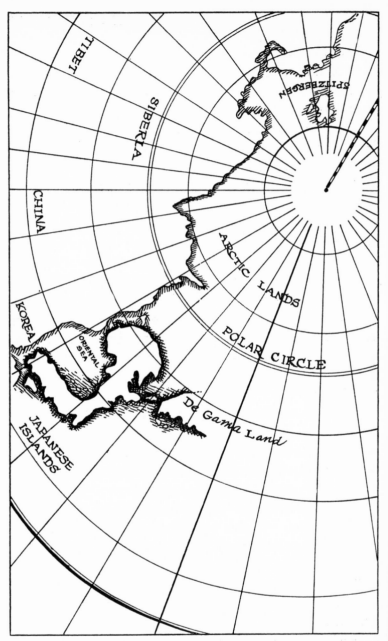

Theoretical location of De Gama Land. The source map for this drawing was the one that led Bering to make this expedition

"But the maps . . ."

"The maps? They are not evidence. We must wait and watch. Perhaps even today—or tomorrow—we shall see with our own eyes."

The weather turned cold and cloudy, but there was little rain, and the sun shone occasionally. The wind remained fresh, blowing out of the north, carrying the vessels along at three or four knots and sometimes as many as seven.

Now and then the *St. Peter* outran the *St. Paul*, and had to clew up the mainsail and foresail in order to wait for the *St. Paul* to come up from astern.

At night the ships often shortened sail and put out two lighted lanterns as a signal to each other that soundings were being taken. But at ninety fathoms no bottom was struck. According to agreement, should either ship find bottom at night, it was to fire a gun and wait for the other to come close by. But as the days passed, no land was found.

On the twelfth of June the wind became unsteady and died, the air cleared, and the sails were clewed to allow for a northerly swell. About noon, Steller and Plenisner were interrupted on the Lookout by Thomas the Hunter, bringing a summons from Bering.

Steller went at once to the cabin. Waxel stood by the stern windows, Yushin and Khitrov by Steller's bunk. Eselberg was sitting on Bering's sea-chest.

The captain-commander himself sat on the stool before his desk, where maps had been spread out. His silver-gray hair fell about his neck, and in the light from the oil lamp his eyes had a cold, forbidding look. Yet his voice had warmth and sincerity.

"We are now eight hundred miles from Avatcha," he

said. "We have proceeded, according to our agreement of May 4th, to the forty-sixth parallel of latitude. And we have seen no sign of the land of De Gama.

"Ever since we passed Vaua Lighthouse we have searched the horizon from sunrise to nightfall, and have found not a trace of land. For two days we have had lookouts in the cross-trees, but they have been silent.

"The question is this: shall we look further or shall we turn toward America? Eselberg, you have studied the maps."

"Aye, Commander," the old navigator said. "I know them better than De Gama himself, I swear it."

"What think you, then?"

"I cannot say." He spread his hands and shrugged his shoulders. "As for De Gama, I would trust him. I would trust all those Spanish explorers, and the Portuguese, too. Aye, we have learned from them ourselves."

Khitrov said: "We have not learned where their land is."

"It is here, I think."

"Where?" Khitrov asked. "We are now east of Japan. Is it part of Japan that they saw?"

"Perhaps, perhaps. It could as well be a part of America."

"But you are not sure?"

"No."

Bering asked Khitrov: "Does the fleet master have an opinion?"

Khitrov smiled and looked around him. "I think we are chasing a fish's tail."

Steller burst out: "Why?"

"All we have come here for is to find a piece of land that is completely mythical. It shows up only on the maps of foreigners. Bah! How can you believe in a piece of fool's paper when our own scouts and explorers—good Russians all, I'll tell you—have already told us where America is?"

"No one," Steller said, "has told you where America is."

Eselberg said: "He is right."

Khitrov frowned. "How can you say he is right? We have records . . ."

"Yes, yes," Eselberg interrupted, "we have all that."

"Well?"

"If we had followed directions, we would have arrived at the edge of America three days after sailing."

Yushin spoke up. "Aye, we all thought America was just across a channel from Siberia. We should have been there now, but we are not."

"We go too far south," Khitrov said. "Wait for the ice to break up in the north, and I will show you."

"Have you been there?" Steller asked the question with an acid tongue, for he knew that Khitrov was speaking from opinion, not experience. "Tell us, Master Khitrov, have you been there?"

Khitrov flushed. "This is a matter for seamen, Herr Steller. We will ask you to listen quietly and not interrupt in these affairs."

Steller turned to Bering. "Am I a servant, not to be heard?"

"What would you tell us?"

Steller addressed himself to Khitrov: "I will tell you this. And it is a nautical matter about which, I will wager, the fleet master has not the slightest knowledge."

The officers laughed. Khitrov's discomfort began to show on his face. Steller went on. "This morning we observed various kinds of seaweed drifting around the ship.

Much of it. You may step out on deck and take a look if you wish, Master Khitrov. I shall be glad to wait!"

"I have seen it. Go on."

"Very well, then. Here is what you do not know: most of that seaweed is known as sea oak. It does not occur very far from the coast because tides always carry it back towards land."

"Are you sure of this?" Bering asked.

"I shall be glad to show you a picture of it and read the Academy description. But that is not necessary. We have also seen gulls, many of them. We have seen terns, and the ducks which they call rock ducks in Kamchatka."

"Then they have come from Kamchatka," said Khitrov.

"Not so, my nautical friend," Steller answered. "These are birds that are never seen in the open sea or far from land."

"Is that proof?"

"No. At least not in itself. But remember, we have seen these things only this morning."

"I have seen lots of birds around the ship, ever since we left Vaua. What have you to say to that?" asked Khitrov.

"I say it proves that you know as much about birds as you accuse me of knowing about the sea!"

There was a burst of laughter and Khitrov reddened with anger. Steller noticed that even Bering's frozen countenance eased a little. A trace of a twinkle appeared in his steely eyes.

"What is your opinion, then?" Bering asked.

"From all the signs, I would say that if the initial course is continued still farther, land will be reached shortly."

Khitrov exploded. "Bah! Are we to let this voyage be guided by one who is not a sailor?"

Bering smiled and said, "We have not heard from the lieutenant."

Waxel had remained quietly by the windows looking out to sea, and had not once turned his head. To all appearances he had not been aware of the proceedings, as if the outcome of the discussion had no bearing upon what would eventually be done, and as if he had already made up his mind.

There was silence in the room, and in a moment Waxel turned slowly. "You have forgotten, have you, the proceedings of our last council meeting?" he asked.

He then took a document from his coat pocket. "I shall read it to you. 'On May 4, 1741, there was a council made up of Captain-Commander Bering, officers, the professor of astronomy, and navigators. After listening to the instructions given to Captain-Commander Bering by the Imperial Admiralty College, it was determined to sail first after leaving Avatcha SE by E, true, and to continue on that rhumb. If no land is found by the time latitude 46 degrees is reached to change the course to E by N steadily until land is discovered.' "

He folded the paper. "We have now reached 46 degrees," he added. "We have no other choice than to change our course for northeast. I am calling the *St. Paul.*"

With that he thrust the paper in his pocket and walked out of the cabin.

Presently there was the loud call of "A-a-ll ha-a-a-nds aloft! Haul down and clew up, my men! We speak the *St. Paul!* Bring this ship to, ye lubbers, bring it to!"

The sails were soon furled and the *St. Peter* turned about to await the arrival of the companion vessel. The *St. Paul* had been laying on the larboard beam, slowly edging away upon the quarter, but now she came nearer and after a while was close enough for conversation. Speaking through the trumpet, Waxel shouted:

"Ahoy, Chikachiev!"

"Ahoy, Waxel!"

"This is the forty-sixth parallel. What say ye to going farther?"

"We have seen no land southeast by east. Have you?"

"No," Waxel answered.

"We could go a little farther. Shall we go another degree?"

"We are willing."

This came as a surprise to Steller, who was not aware that Waxel would follow anything else than council decisions. But then the lieutenant on the *St. Paul* said:

"Very well. But the wind is contrary today and we make little headway."

"Sail ye north by east till the wind be favorable."

"Aye, aye! Northeast it is!"

The crew sprang aloft to loose the sails and brace the yards. Thus the ship made sail again, turning slowly toward the northeast.

Steller returned crestfallen to the Lookout. His shoulders were bent and he held his hat in his hand. Plenisner was busily sketching some ducks that had been flying past the ship.

"I can see by the look on your face," Plenisner said, "that things have not gone as you wished."

Steller did not answer.

"Now cheer up, old man!" the artist consoled. "It is not as bad as you think."

Steller slumped into the chair. "Just at the time," he said, "when they must apply reason in order to attain the wished-for object, their erratic behavior begins. I do not know why they are so thick-headed! They sneer and ridicule and leave totally unheeded every opinion offered by anybody not a seaman."

"Tut. That is no way for them to act."

"I told them about the seaweed, and the ducks. It was no use. They must believe that with the rules of navigation they have also acquired all other science and logic."

"Well, then, I shall work an evil curse upon them."

"This day might have been decisive for the whole enterprise."

"Shall I cast a cruel spell upon all the officers, or merely on Khitrov?"

Steller frowned. Then he looked up at Plenisner and laughed. "You are a scoundrel," he said. "You're not much help, are you?"

"I'm trying to be. Oh well, back to my beloved birds. I guess I'm not a politician either!"

One by one Steller talked with the men on board as he had with farmers down the country lanes near Wittenberg. He talked to the sailors as they swabbed the decks. He interrupted their work as they slushed the mast, or calked the decks, or scraped rust from the chain cables.

Down below, the steerage was crowded, and men had to sleep in close quarters with coils of rigging, spare canvas, piled chains, and their own duffel. Steller spent many hours with the soldiers and sailors and grenadiers. He told them of Europe and gave them news of the outside world which they had not had during their confinement in Siberia.

"Here, let me give you a hand with that!" was his way of opening a conversation, and it did not matter what the man was doing—mending clothes, repairing canvas, oiling boots, or even tarring down the standing rigging—Steller would "lend a hand" and they would talk.

"The men need someone to talk to besides their own kind," he would say.

The result of this project was twofold: one, the forecastle on the Sabbath became a crowded place where in the salty wind of the North Pacific Steller spoke of God's benevolent power over the sea and the men who sailed it; and two, the men now had a new respect for him.

"Did ye see that!" asked a sailor as Steller walked away from him once. "He tarred the rigging with me. Got his hands dirty as bilge-tar, and laughing he was all the time!"

He left a Yakut rifleman aghast by pulling the soldier's gun to pieces, cleaning it, and reassembling it without the slightest hesitation.

The assistant surgeon stood open-mouthed as Steller sorted the medicines in the ship's chest, named them, catalogued their uses, and prescribed the treatment for all known ship's fevers.

Steller confounded the Siberian carpenters by describing at length the merits of various woods, recalling the construction of the church and barracks and other buildings at Avatcha, and telling why certain kinds of wood were used in certain places. Asked one of the carpenters: "And he is from the Academy of Sciences?"

"Yes."

"He is an Adjunct?"

"Yes."

"I do not believe it. He is one of us."

This admiration was not shared by the officers. Plenisner thought that they were jealous.

"Nonsense," Steller said. "These officers lived for ten years in Siberia. They did as they pleased and demanded and received so much homage from everyone that now they are in the habit of thinking themselves infallible."

"You think so?" the artist asked.

"Certainly. They feel insulted when you mention anything of which they are ignorant."

"Then they'll have nothing to do with you? Well, well, well! Perhaps you are better off. You owe them nothing!"

Steller held up a finger. "Don't forget that we want to get to America. And without taking all summer at it!"

Headed north by east now, the two ships sailed on toward America. The winds increased, still chilly and damp.

"It's a fair wind now," said Eselberg, buttoning his coat against the chill, "and plenty!"

One evening Steller went to the cabin; he found Bering sitting at the table, studying the maps.

"Will you have a cup of tea, Commander?"

The Dane nodded, and in a few moments Steller had prepared a pot over the oil flame. In silence they sipped their tea, sweetened with a little molasses. Outside the wind shrieked, and rain began to patter against the windows.

"It may be a big storm," Steller ventured.

Bering rose slowly and went to his bunk. "The Pacific is a strange ocean," he said, quietly. "Many things we are told about it. We know very little. It may be a full storm now. In another minute the sky will be clear."

Steller could not sleep that night. The roar of the wind outside, the creak of the timbers and grinding of the beams, the motion and settling of the cargo—sounding as a dull boom-boom from deep within the vessel—

raked across his senses, pounding into his brain all kinds of conjectures. He knew that these were matters for the seamen and the officers. But he could not help wondering if the chain plates were properly fastened, if the compasses were corrected, if the foremast had been sufficiently strengthened. Nothing must delay their getting to America!

And then, too, he could hear Khitrov's voice coming to him as if in a dream: "You should not concern yourself with nautical matters. You should not concern yourself . . ." After awhile he rose in the darkness and put on his coat.

As Bering had predicted, the night sky was clear and the stars were shining, though the wind still blew at gale force, singing like violins through the rigging.

It was Yushin's watch. The rotund second mate sat beneath the lantern in the quarterdeck cabin, head in his hand, writing in the Log:

"*St. Paul* NW, 2 miles; lowered main-staysail; clear with passing clouds; hauled up the weather clew of the foresail."

He looked up as Steller entered.

"Ah, the Adjunct. Come in. I see you cannot sleep. Is it the wind?"

"I suppose so," Steller replied.

"You will get used to it after a while. A ship is a place where there is always noise and movement. Things are never quiet. It is hard to accustom oneself to it."

Steller seated himself on a map case. "It is more than that which keeps me awake."

"What then?"

"When America appears out there on the horizon, I want to know it. I want to see it."

"But we have lookouts. They will inform us."

"Yes, but it still keeps me awake. To know we are so close, to expect any minute a cry of land."

"A sailor becomes accustomed to these things."

"I am not a sailor. But I love the sea."

"What are you, really, Herr Steller?"

Steller paused. As he recalled, he had not been asked that question in just that way before. "The ship's list calls me a mineralogist," he said.

"Are you?"

"Yes, of course."

"But you are more. They say you can pull a soldier's gun apart and restore it again. Have you been a soldier?"

"I was with the Russian Army."

"As a soldier?"

"I was a physician."

"A physician!" Yushin leaned closer on the desk. "I thought so. The assistant surgeon says you know medicine better than he."

The wind screamed loudly outside. Steller said: "One is always a doctor. It is one of those things to which a man dedicates his life—to save lives, to heal the sick. You, my dear Yushin, are dedicated to the sea in much the same way."

"And what else, Herr Steller? You interest me greatly. What else? You are a minister."

"No, no. I have studied theology, that is all."

"But you have preached? You have given sermons?"

"Yes."

"It is the same thing. What else have you done?"

"Come now," Steller said, rising, "we talk too much of me. And I am unimportant."

"Except as pertains to America?"

Steller beamed. "There is much to be done there."

Yushin smiled, his blue eyes twinkling in his round face. "I can understand you better now. To a sailor, the ship is home. But to you . . ."

At this point a lookout burst into the room. "Mate Yushin!" he said. "Something is wrong!"

"What is it?" Yushin queried. "Speak out, man!"

"The lights have gone!"

"What lights? What lights? What are you talking about?"

The man caught his breath. "The lights of the *St. Paul,* sir," he said. "The *St. Paul* is not in sight!"

Yushin leaped to his feet. "What?" he said, his voice rising to a high pitch. "You've lost their lights?"

"Yes, sir."

"Are you sure?"

"Yes, sir. We've looked all around."

"You idiot!" Yushin shouted, his face whitening. "She was just northwest of us."

"Yes, sir. I know, sir. But her lights are gone."

Yushin clapped on his hat. "Do you know what this means? We must not lose the *St. Paul!*"

Yushin swept the lookout aside, saying: "Be off, fool!" Moving as rapidly as his stout form allowed, he swept out of the cabin and onto the deck. Steller followed.

There was nothing to be seen. It was as dark as the darkest night, and save for the twinkling of the stars and the utterly faint line of the horizon, the sea was barren of any sign of the *St. Peter's* sister ship.

Yushin pointed to the northwest. "There! That's where the *St. Paul* was. But there is nothing there. Quick! The spy glass!"

With the glass he scanned the darkness in all directions. "Ahoy, lookout," he said. "When did you first notice this disappearance?"

"Half an hour ago, sir."

"Why didn't you tell me?"

"We thought her lantern might have gone out, sir. In this wind . . ."

"You were ordered to tell me!"

"She may have had to heave to under the mizzensail, sir."

Yushin shouted: "You do not do the thinking on this ship, pig!" He strode over to the rail and grasped the stanchions, saying in a quavering voice: "What shall we do?"

"If I were you," Steller volunteered, "I would inform the commander."

Yushin turned. "Bering? No. Not Bering."

Steller was taken aback. "Why not?" he asked.

Yushin did not answer. Instead he turned to the lookout and barked out an order. "You, pig! Get Lieutenant Waxel up here at once!"

The lookout departed, and Yushin strode quickly back to the cabin, Steller following.

The second mate reached beneath the log book and took from the desk a slim leather-bound folio. His hands were trembling slightly. "The signal code," he said. "There are prescribed rules for this. We must follow them."

Waxel strode into the room, and Yushin poured out to him all that had happened, stressing the fact that the lookouts had allowed the lights of the *St. Paul* to disappear. Waxel issued orders in a sharp, curt voice: "Hang one lantern at the mainmast and another at the foreshrouds on the larboard side. Fire one gun."

"Yes, sir," Yushin said.

"Clew up the foresail. Set the mainstaysail. Heave to."

Waxel turned on his heel and was about to leave when Steller caught his arm: "You will inform the commander?"

For a moment Waxel looked at him icily, and Steller did not know what to make of the silence. Then, without a word, the lieutenant was gone.

Steller returned to the darkened cabin. Bering was asleep. For a moment he pondered whether to wake the captain and tell him what had happened. Losing the *St. Paul* was a serious matter. The captain—of all people—should know.

But Steller hesitated. Command in the Russian navy was curious. He could not understand it. The captain had little real power. Everything had to be decided in council. All the officers had to agree. Maybe that's why Yushin and Waxel had not awakened Bering. Perhaps they wanted to handle things themselves.

"Oh, well, let them!" Steller thought. "It's a funny way to run a navy."

He crawled beneath his blanket and drifted into a fitful sleep. Once he thought he heard someone talking quietly to Bering, but he was not sure.

The sun rose, and the *St. Paul* was not in sight. With lookouts at the topmast, scanning the sea in every direction, the *St. Peter* turned about and sailed on the reverse course. For hours the wind howled across the icy sea without sign of let-up, but not the slightest hint of the *St. Paul* was to be seen. Finally, with the wind increasing, the *St. Peter* was forced to take in sail for safety.

Night came and went, and on the following morning

the wind diminished a little. Sails were unfurled and the vessel resumed the search.

For three days they sailed back toward the mythical De Gama Land, but no land was sighted, and no ship.

"So, Herr Steller," Khitrov said, with a sneer, "your De Gama Land, or whatever you want to call it, has vanished into thin air. What do you make of it now, eh? Ha, ha, ha!" His bulky frame shook as he laughed.

The color rose in Steller's face. "If you had listened to me in the first place—"

"To you!" Khitrov laughed scornfully. "You are a landsman. What do you know of sailing matters?"

"—and had guided yourself by the signs in the sea," Steller went on, "you would very likely have been at land by now."

"Bah, it is a waste of time to pursue this course any more! The *St. Paul* is lost. We are on our own. And we can get along without your help, Herr Doktor!"

On June twenty-third, Bering, Waxel, and Khitrov, meeting in council, decided to resume a northerly course as before. Whereupon the *St. Peter* was turned about.

With full sail she plunged into the turbulent waves, flinging spray from her bows. Once more the sailors climbed aloft and braced the yards and tumbled down sail. Once more the *St. Peter,* alone now, was entering a strange, mysterious, unknown segment of the North Pacific Ocean.

๙ 7 ๒

ALASKA

STEADILY the *St. Peter* sailed across the Pacific, past drift-wood and seaweed that suggested land, but never in sight of land itself. Somewhere in the emptiness of the North Pacific rose the ramparts of America. Somewhere ahead lay a land whose northern shores no European had ever trod; no chart gave a direction, no log a distance, no table a depth.

Steller and Plenisner kept watch for telltale signs in the sea, sitting at their lookout for hours at a time.

Steller carried a copy of *Robinson Crusoe*. As the days went by he read it aloud and those who wished to listen came to the Lookout and sat beside him or around him. At times his audience swelled to more than thirty men, most of whom could neither read nor write, but all of whom could listen as if transfixed.

Between times Steller and Plenisner continued to study the sea intently.

When it became apparent that the driftwood that passed the vessel nearly every day was coming from the lee, Steller was sure that land was near.

He told Khitrov: "See for yourself. There!" He pointed aft. "Driftwood from the north. If you do not believe what I say, there is the proof. Sail north and you anchor." But Khitrov only gave a contemptuous snarl and walked away.

As June turned into July, thick fog and chilly rain swept over the open water. Sometimes heavy seas tossed the *St. Peter* like a float on a fisherman's net, and raw winds blew down from the polar regions.

On rare days the sky changed and became a clear expanse of delicate blue, with thin pale clouds skirting the horizon. On such a day Steller thought of spreading a bearskin over the forecastle and napping in the noonday sun, but then quickly discarded the idea. I'm getting lazy! he thought.

Once he watched Eselberg standing the wheel watch and wondered what had brought the old man, now nearly seventy years old, to the sea. According to the crewmen, he was the best helmsman that ever put hand to spoke. But that had been long ago.

At length Georg Wilhelm grew impatient, and said so to Eselberg. "Yah, I know," the navigator replied, "and so am I, and so is everyone else."

"It has been weeks since we left Avatcha. The question now is—will we ever see land at all?"

"Of course!" Eselberg chided him for his doubts. "You are impetuous, my boy. You would cross the sea as if it were only a musket-shot wide."

"We have gone enough to the northeast," Steller said. "Let us now turn directly north."

Bering agreed, but Steller thought that the commander was merely being kind. When Bering returned to the cabin after a ship's council, he would spread his hands in resignation: "They have voted to go straight ahead."

At last the ship entered a part of the sea where debris

of various sorts was seen floating on the water. Gulls whirled in spiral tracks and alighted on the ship.

With this Steller went to Yushin: "Today we saw large flocks of gulls sitting on the water."

"Yes?"

"Gulls are excellent indicators of land. If you turn north, for a few hours . . ."

Yushin held up his hand. "My dear Adjunct, gulls fly everywhere. You cannot count on them to bring us land."

"But we have seen jellyfish and sea grass. If they don't come from land, where do they come from?"

Yushin closed the log book. "There are many things about the sea that we do not understand. We sail by the wind yet the wind does not always help us. We lose the *St. Paul* because we do not know how to save ourselves from the storm. If we make mistakes they are things we cannot anticipate. You have spent your life on land. You are not a seaman and do not understand the sea; it is as simple as that. You have not been in God's council chamber."

In the cabin at night, as he lay with his head on his tunic, Steller said to Bering: "Gulls are gulls and such quantities of seaweed must certainly mean land."

The commander shrugged. "In many parts of the ocean," he said, "the whole sea is overgrown with weeds. What can you say to that?"

"Plants in the tropics move differently than they do here. You cannot judge the American coast by what you see elsewhere."

Bering closed his eyes. "And can you?"

They sailed on without sighting land, and the more they sailed the more puzzled Eselberg became.

"We should have come to America in a few days," he

said. "But look at us! Weeks we have sailed, and a thousand times we have thrown overboard the weight, but not so much as a sniff of bottom at 180 fathoms." He shook his head. "It is too much for me."

"I have made my position clear to them," Steller said, with a sigh of despair. "But in their eyes I am just like a cossack freighting provisions from Yakutsk to Okhotsk. I might as well be an exile who obeys without back talk."

Eselberg rubbed his chin thoughtfully. "You say you have seen large flocks of gulls?"

"Yes!"

"And seaweed?"

"Much of it, and driftwood."

"You have told this to everybody?"

"To everybody. To Yushin, to Waxel, to Khitrov, to everybody."

"And Bering?"

"And Bering."

Eselberg put his hands on his hips and looked up to the sky. "I will see what I can do."

Before the next ship's council could be held, however, seals were sighted. So were sea otters, floating on their backs, arms crossed on their bosoms, webbed toes turned upward, tails straight out. Plenisner chuckled as he sketched them.

There they were for all to see. On July 11th shouts were heard on deck and Steller rushed out to see a dead whale floating past. On it were many gulls.

On July 14th, Bering, Waxel, Khitrov, and Eselberg held ship's council, and this time when Eselberg found Steller on the forecastle, he was smiling.

"We are turning north," he said. "Half our supply of water is gone, and whatever is left will be gone before

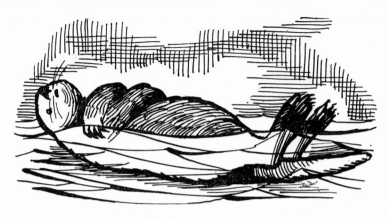

Alaskan sea otter

September. Besides, we have no way of knowing if the barrels in the lower hold are full or if some of the water has leaked out. If we go east, we go away from Kamchatka and so cannot return by September. If that happens we suffer great hardships and, may God preserve us, extreme misfortune."

"How well we know that!"

"It was agreed that if we go north, we have a better chance of finding water."

Georg Wilhelm sighed and said, "Ah, yes, as I have been saying for weeks."

The next morning, after breakfast of groats and hardtack, Steller went to the forecastle again. A topsail wind was blowing, and looking up he saw that all the sails were set.

"A good westerly wind, Esel," he said.

"Aye, lad," Eselberg said, "and plenty; but not for long. She is unsteady today. Maybe that is a good sign, yah?"

As Eselberg predicted, the wind soon died away and a

calm settled over the ocean. In it the *St. Peter* glided like a silent phantom; from the bow, Steller scanned the enclosing mists in all directions, but saw and heard nothing.

For hours he listened to the waves lapping against the bows, and watched the sea and the fog. Seals and sea otters appeared in the mist, briefly, transient, playful for a while, and then were gone.

Plenisner had gone below early in the morning, into the steerage, and returned now looking glum. "Bad time with the crew," he said.

"The crew?" Steller asked.

"Everybody's grumbling. We've all been cramped so long. The men grumble about being brought along on an exploring expedition and finding nothing to explore."

"How can we blame them for that?"

The wind had come again, and the sailors were mounting the yards and letting down the sails. The *St. Peter* moved ahead.

Plenisner stretched against a pile of canvas. "They say if we don't sight land in five days the ship will sail for home."

"Home?" Steller said. "Did we come here to turn like cowards and head for home? We have a job to do."

"We have not turned back yet."

"Nor shall we! By God's grace we embarked upon this expedition and . . . if it . . . be . . ."

His voice trailed off. He stared toward the northeast.

Plenisner looked up. "What do you see?"

Steller did not answer, but rose slowly to his feet, keeping his eyes focussed on the horizon line—a misty, cloud-swept scene, dimmed in the lowering sun.

Now be careful, he thought. You are not sure; and nothing must be said until you are certain. You have been watching so long. It is nothing, it is nothing. Clouds and nothing more. Wait until you can see better, until morning. Wait until you are sure . . .

"In Heaven's name, old man," Plenisner prompted, "why are you staring like that?"

The clouds are tricky. Oh, where is that infernal glass? And where is Thomas when I need him? After weeks of staring into fleeting shapes and empty seas . . . Don't let your eyes fool you now. No doubt some . . .

Then Steller dashed for the rail and gripped it, giving a hoarse shout.

"La-a-a-nd! La-a-a-nd! Dead ahead!"

Plenisner sprang to the rail beside him. "Where?" he asked.

"It's gone," Steller said.

The ship was in commotion. Steller's shout spread across the deck and the news sputtered like wildfire from dozens of lips amid echoes of "Land ahoy!" and "Where away?"

Waxel called for his spyglass. Men streamed to the rails, leaped atop the windlasses and forecastle, sprang into the rigging and hoisted themselves astride the yards to see for themselves. Steller pointed and new shouts arose.

"La-a-and ho-o-o!" came the long-drawn-out cry in the happy voices of the sailors. Then darkness closed in and clouds covered the scene.

"Is it visions, now, Herr Steller?" Khitrov scoffed. "Ach! Where is your land now? Methinks your eyes play tricks upon you!"

Steller scowled: "Put down your line and touch bottom ere you scrape your keel, I warn you!"

Waxel put away his spyglass and said: "If we have come to land it will stay where it is until morning."

But their skepticism hardly extended to the ship's company. That night the *St. Peter* was a ship of exploration again, with as jubilant a crew as ever sailed the North Pacific.

All night long Steller could not sleep nor get out of his mind the shapes he had seen in the mist. The thing was not a dream! It couldn't be!

Long before dawn he dressed and went on deck. An unbroken silence reigned over the sky and sea, and nothing was to be heard but muted rippling at the cut-water.

Over and over the outlines of the mountains came to him as in a dream, and with them the haunting fear that the horizon had played some trick on him after all.

July 16th broke with unsettled weather, and the horizon could not be seen. Clouds scudded low overhead, and after a while there were openings through which the sun shone. At any moment it seemed as if the clouds might rise.

Steller ate nothing, not daring to leave his vigil. By 12:30 the clouds had lifted a little and grown thin, and the sun came out, shining across the choppy sea. Steller and Plenisner stood silently at the rail—which was lined with crewmen, sailors, soldiers, cooks, and servants—and felt the cool breezes that swept through the rigging.

And then Steller said quietly, as if to himself: "There it is!"

In a few seconds the clouds unrolled above a panorama of snow-clad mountains and towering peaks such as few of the onlookers had ever seen. As far as the eye could see stretched a high and rugged coastal range, majestic, sweeping, immense, dominated by a lofty volcano and snow-capped ridges to the northwest!

For a moment the only sounds were the sighing of

wind through the rigging and the lap of water against the ship, the creaking of timbers, the rustle of heavy canvas in the breeze. A gull flew overhead, but made no sound.

The sailors seemed transfixed, staring and seeing, but unbelieving. And then came one long shout, and after that, many.

Steller gripped the stanchions until his knuckles whitened. He leaped up on a windlass and said: "It's unexplored, and it's ours! Look! At the base of the mountain; what beautiful forests."

Khitrov stood on the quarterdeck, scanning the mountains through a glass, and Steller could not resist the opportunity. "Ahoy, Master Khitrov, do you see it now? D'you need the glass? Dead ahead, dead ahead!"

And then Steller turned and said, "Where is the captain?"

They found Bering in his cabin, lying in bed, eyes closed.

"Have you not heard, Captain?" Steller said. "We have come to land."

Bering opened his eyes and looked around. Presently he spoke, quietly. "I have heard."

"Then do you not wish to see where we have come?"

Slowly, Bering rose from bed and made his way out of the cabin and onto the quarterdeck. For a long while he gazed at the scene, but no flicker of emotion crossed his countenance. He shrugged his shoulders slightly and, without a word, turned and walked away.

Steller and Plenisner exchanged glances of surprise. In a moment they followed him into the cabin.

"It is a great day for us, is it not?" Bering asked. They nodded. "We have come to America and we have done our duty and carried out our orders to the best of our

ability. Gentlemen, the mission of the Admiralty is fulfilled. We think now we have accomplished everything
and many go about inflated, but they do not consider
where we have reached land, how far we are from home,
and what may yet happen; who knows but that perhaps
trade winds may arise, which may prevent us from returning? We do not know this country; nor are we provided
with supplies for a wintering."

He paused, and Steller could hear the cries of the
exultant crewmen. If Bering heard them, he gave no sign.

"We must stay here no longer than to take on water,"
he said. "This is July sixteenth. We must make Kamchatka by September, or perish."

They soon discovered that the nearest harbor of any
sort lay in the lee of an island that projected toward them
from the mainland. High cliffs rose above the shore and
ended in a ridge that dropped sharply off at the seaward
end of the island. Beyond the point, which they named
Cape St. Elias after the Saint of the day, a dark gray
pinnacle rock rose sharply out of the sea—like a giant
lighthouse whose top had been lost in a gale.

For three days, with the weather changing time and
again, the *St. Peter* was tacked in and out in an effort to
get under the lee of the island. Soundings were taken
repeatedly. Fog and low clouds hampered the operation,
as did heavy rain and contrary and variable winds, but at
last the vessel moved cautiously among the reefs.

Then, on the fourth day, when they had gone as close
as they dared, the sails were furled and the anchor let go.
Then, while water casks were being made ready, Bering
instructed Khitrov to assemble a crew in the longboat and
examine the strait ahead for safe passage.

Route of the *St. Peter*—from Kamchatka to Kayak Island and then to Shumagin Islands (see Chapter 9)

Steller was elated. "Thomas," he said, "get our gear and stow it in the longboat. Tell Plenisner to bring his kit to the forecastle at once and prepare to . . ."

"No." It was Bering's voice.

Steller turned. "What did you say?"

Bering smiled. "There will be so little room."

"But . . ." Steller was stunned.

"The purpose of the boat trip is to find passage and a water source. When that is done Khitrov will return. Perhaps you can go then."

"But I propose to go ashore and remain until the water is aboard."

"That is not safe. This is only an island."

"Is there no intention of landing on the mainland?"

"We do not know if we can."

"Well, then," Steller said, "if I was signed on the expedition to examine the country, I must go ashore at once. I am an Adjunct of the Academy, on Imperial Order, remember. This work is imperative."

The captain-commander's eyes were expressionless. "Yes. We are very much aware of that. And so is ours."

"Then," Steller drew himself up, "my hunter and I must not delay."

"I am afraid not, my son. We must take on water and get under way."

"Under way? Have we come for the express purpose of carrying American water to Asia, Commander? I must warn you . . ."

Again Bering smiled. "I alone am responsible for the safety of the crew and for the safe return of the expedition."

"I do not think that has anything to do with me. My orders are Imperial Orders."

"Going ashore means great danger," Bering said. "We have heard of savages living in these woods. They are said to attack people without warning and cut them to pieces."

"I must remind you, Commander, that I am not so womanish as to fear danger. If you will recall it, I traveled across the whole of Russia and Siberia, and have had my share of what you call danger."

"I am sorry; it is still impossible."

"Impossible? Going ashore is in line with my principal work and duty and it is my determination to serve the Crown to the best of my ability. You cannot mean 'impossible.' " He took a step forward. "Now if your officers will allow us to descend into the boat—"

The crewmen had gathered at the sound of the voices, and the officers had come to the quarterdeck. Eselberg wore a puzzled expression, as if the whole thing were too much for him to understand. Khitrov and Waxel were without expression, their caps pulled low. Yushin seemed a trifle frightened. Off to one side Plenisner was concealing a smile, as if the entire affair were a comedy to which he had been admitted without invitation.

"It is impossible," Bering repeated.

"I beg of you," Steller said, his face flushed with anger. "If I am denied, you risk reprimand when we return. I must warn you, sir."

Bering reached out to place his arm on Steller's shoulder. "Come, come now. Perhaps we can discuss it later. You must not be a wild man. Why, see here! Chocolate is being served up by the cook, chocolate that we have brought all the way from St. Petersburg for this occasion. Would you be held back by business when chocolate is at hand?"

Steller stepped back.

"You fool!" he said. "Is this the stupidity for which you were made captain of this ship?"

The crewmen gasped. Yushin turned white. Steller went on: "I am going ashore. If you try to stop me, you will be reported to the Academy and to the Crown directly. And I shall recommend that you be stricken in rank and clapped in irons!"

Steller's long frame shook as he spat the words.

Gasps of astonishment came from the crew. Khitrov fingered his gloves nervously. Eselberg opened his mouth in surprise.

Bering's face gave not a hint of his reaction to the outburst. Eselberg raged inwardly at Steller's impertinence. What impudence! he thought. This young fool will be put in irons, if he is lucky enough to get off as easily as that.

Even Plenisner had lost his smile. His eyes were wide with disbelief.

At length the captain-commander's face broke into a wrinkled smile, and he nodded resignation.

"I think I could not keep you from going, even if you had to swim. You are young and ill-tempered, as I was myself; as we all were. I am an old man, and it is not upon me to judge. So go if you must, but at ten, with the water yawl."

At this, Steller turned on his heel. "I wait on no one." He motioned to Thomas and the two of them clambered over the side of the ship and down into the longboat where the sailors were waiting.

Quickly Bering called the trumpeters to the rail and bade them sound a royal flourish. How loud it was! Steller halted, not quite sure whether the bugles had sounded in mockery or in earnest.

As echoes of the trumpets faded, every man aboard burst into laughter. And as Steller, red-faced, looked back from the longboat, he could see Friedrich Plenisner laughing hardest of all.

৶ 8 ৶

KAYAK ISLAND

THE SAILORS rowed toward shore, heading for a break in the woods at the base of a thickly forested slope. The trunks of fallen trees, white as scattered bones against the dark timber, hinted of a stream, and soon they saw one, a small creek that tumbled over loose, gray boulders down to the shore.

Steller saw no sign of life. As they neared shore he scanned the rocky beach in both directions, hoping to see smoke from an Indian camp, or some indication that the island was inhabited.

The forest stole silently down toward shore, a thick tangle of trees so deep as to be almost impenetrable, so easily capable, he thought, of concealing well-armed Indians. He shaded his eyes and sought to make out movement within the dark shadows of the forest, but saw nothing.

History does not record the exact moment the boat nudged the gravelly beach. It was the moment Georg Wilhelm Steller had waited for. We may presume that his eagerness—born of a decade of dreams and plans—prompted him to leap from the boat before it had stopped. If so, then Steller was the first naturalist, and the first

European, to set foot in what would later be called Alaska.

After making sure that Khitrov would send the water boat to this point on account of the stream, he and Thomas struck off down the beach, striding on their unconditioned sea legs, wobbling at first like turkeys.

What a clear and beautiful day it was! There was hardly a cloud in the sky.

"We haven't much time," Steller said. "We must find out as much as we can about this island and any people who live here. Keep your eyes open."

"Yes, Master."

Suddenly Thomas pointed to a tall tree standing upon a small rise away from the beach. "There is something under that tree, Master. It looks like smoke!"

They quickened their pace. "You're right. There has been a fire here."

Steller knelt and picked up an old piece of log, hollowed out in the shape of a trough. "Indians!" he said, excitedly. "They cooked their food here and left, not two hours ago. Look there! Bones, with bits of meat on them."

"What kind of bones, Master?"

"Reindeer. Maybe. Unless I am mistaken, the mainland is good caribou country. The Indians must bring their meat here to the island."

"Why?"

Steller shrugged. "Come," he said, and they pushed on, clambering over rocks that littered the beach like broken toadstools.

Hardly had they gone another mile when they discovered a trail leading into the woods.

"Wait," Steller said, placing his hand on the hunter's shoulder. Overhead the wind sighed through the needles of the trees as if the very ghosts of Indians were swinging among the branches. Far back on the beach they could hear faintly the sounds of the sailors casting off to return to the *St. Peter*. "How are you armed?"

Thomas carried a loaded gun, and in addition had a knife and an axe. Steller was armed only with a dagger, the purpose of which was to pry rocks loose and dig up plants.

Quietly he said: "We are not armed to the teeth, and we could not long fight our way from a trap if we were. When we meet the Indians we may have time to greet them, and I will use a Kamchadal dialect or two in the hope that they will understand. But make no move that they will think warlike. Do you understand?"

"Yes."

They entered the forest and at once were engulfed in gloom. Pungent pine fragrance assailed them, as did the dankness of the forest floor. They had scarcely moved a dozen steps when they came upon a barricade of pine branches.

"They have tried to block the path," Steller whispered. "But see how crude a barrier it is! We must have surprised them. They cannot be far ahead."

They walked quietly along the trail, and around them the dimness of the deep woods closed in, pierced only by shafts of sunlight.

The trail forked, dividing into several paths and, for a time, the naturalist and hunter explored these through the wood. Along one of them they came to an open space in the trees, and saw that the ground had been covered with cut grass.

"Aha!" Steller said. "See what we have here!"

He knelt and pushed the grass aside, uncovering a layer of rocks.

"A cache!" Thomas whispered.

"We're in luck. But keep watch, Thomas. If we are caught here the natives will have good reason to shoot us without asking questions."

Steller went to work removing the rocks that topped the cache. It was an elaborate one, rectangular in shape, about eighteen feet long and twelve feet wide.

Deeper and deeper he dug, coming upon all manner of things: utensils made of bark and filled with smoked red salmon, a quantity of sweet grass, plant fibers for making fish nets, rolls of dried inner bark of the spruce tree, and bales of seaweed thongs which he tested and found to be of unusual strength and firmness.

Under these he came upon a sight that sent a shiver down his spine—a bundle of large and dangerous-looking arrows.

"We had better take what we need as scientific specimens," he said, "and get out of here. The owners may think we are stealing all their possessions and put a few of their arrows through us!"

He withdrew two bundles of fish, the arrows, some fire-making apparatus, a bundle of thongs, and a little of the bark and grass.

"Take these to the beach," he told Thomas. "The water boat should be there now. Go aboard the *St. Peter* and tell the captain-commander to give you gifts for the Indians, and two or three men to help us. Tell him what we have found and that I am on the trail of the Indians."

"But, Master . . ."

"Advise the men on the beach to be alert for attack."

"Master, you must take my gun."

"No."

"But I will not need it along the shore."

"Nor will I in the mountains."

"What if you meet the natives?"

"I hope to talk to them, not shoot them."

"But . . ."

"Away with you! The sun grows higher!"

Thomas disappeared quickly into the gloom of the forest.

Steller re-covered the cache; then he made his way back to the shore, trying not to remember the sharp edges of the arrows he had seen. Turning left at the water's edge, he struck off in the direction in which he and Thomas had been headed before they turned into the woods.

For what seemed like hours—though he had little impression of how time was passing—he walked down the beach. Fish had washed ashore, strange kinds he had not seen before. There were also clams and snails and pieces of driftwood.

He picked up rocks and handfuls of sand and examined them with a small lens. What insects he saw crawling among the rocks he caught and placed in folded scraps of paper. Tiny flowers, their delicate petals open to the sun, were lifted gently from the soil, roots and all, and placed between small blotters in a packet held together with leather straps.

In his black leather bag was a single bottle of spirits into which he placed small minnows, spiders, and other delicate creatures.

With his dagger he probed in the deep, rich soil beneath the trees that edged the shore. Above him, he heard, flitting through the branches, a bird that he could never quite see. Its raucous, scolding calls, however, were clearly meant for him. He was an intruder in the bird's domain, and was being invited out! The bird was persistent, and

once Steller thought he saw a flash of blue as the chattering bird flew deeper into the woods.

Before he knew it he had come to a promontory ex-
tending so far into the sea beyond the beach that he could
go no farther.

A hill rose steeply to landward and with some difficulty
he ascended it. This vantage point gave him a commanding view of the island, which would come to be known
as Kayak Island, and of the sea. Offshore the *St. Peter*
lay at anchor, and the yawl, like a tiny water beetle in
the deep blue ocean, headed toward shore, leaving a slim
white wake behind it.

Then Steller turned and looked about him. The far
side of the hill that he had climbed dropped off abruptly
in a steep face down which descent was impossible.

So where then? The next course would be to turn
south, toward the other side of the island, to see if a river
and harbor existed on that side.

He started down the mountain but presently came to
the edge of a dark and tangled forest into which no trace
of a path existed.

Steller paused. If he entered this almost impassable
forest, Thomas would have trouble tracking him. It would
also be too far away in case some discovery had to be
made known to Bering at once. And the farther he traveled, the less chance there was of returning before nightfall.

As he climbed to the crest of the hill again, puffing and
stifling his disappointment, his eyes fixed upon a movement on a spruce-covered hill scarcely a mile away. It
was a spiral of smoke!

The Americans! Steller's heart leaped at the prospect
of meeting them.

His first impulse was to drop pack and instruments and rush instantly to the campsite, for here, right at hand, was his chance to meet the people and make a complete report on them.

But the impulse was checked as soon as it arose.

"That would be folly," he thought. Nevertheless his spirits had risen considerably, and, spinning abruptly, he plunged down the steep slope and raced through the forest to the shore.

Yushin was just loading all hands into the water boat. "Sit down, sit down!" he said, as Steller arrived, nearly collapsing in the water. "How many miles have you run? Is something after you?"

"No, no," Steller gasped, "but I must get word to the commander."

"About what? We are just leaving. Will you go with us?"

"No, no. Tell him I have discovered the natives."

"Where?"

"Smoke from a campsite, not six versts (four miles) away."

"Will they attack?"

"I intend to go meet them."

"Herr Steller! You are mad! They have weapons!"

"I know. I know. I cannot go to them alone. Advise Bering that I need a yawl and two or three men besides Thomas and myself. Tell him to send gifts for the natives. Night is coming and we must make all haste."

After the boat had cast off, Steller sat exhausted on the beach, and only then did he set his packsack aside. He was tired, terribly tired.

In a little while he made a tea from the delicious water

of the stream that tumbled down to the shore. Taking a scrap of paper from his plant bag he jotted down notes on what he had seen.

There was so much! Where would he begin? He wrote in Latin, laboring with cumbersome scientific names, entering descriptions and comparisons, and making notes.

On the next boat trip Thomas returned.

"Here are the things you wanted, Master," he said. He produced an iron kettle, a Chinese pipe, a piece of Chinese silk, and a pound of tobacco.

"Where are the men?"

"There are none, Master."

"No one to help us?"

"No, sir. And . . ."

"What else?"

"We are ordered to return to the ship at once."

Steller exploded: "At once? At once, does he say? Now is that not a patriotic and courteous reply?"

"The commander said to place the gifts in the cache and return on the water boat or he would forget about us."

"Ah!" Steller flung his head back and laughed. "Does he not know that that would suit me just fine?"

He walked a few steps down to the surf, where the boat had been beached. "Thomas," he said, "God gives each of us the time, and the place, and the opportunity to do that which he is ordered to do."

"Yes, sir."

"He expects us to present our services favorably to the highest authorities. We have come a long way, and have waited a long time, and have cost untold expenses to the Empress, all to do as we are instructed. We shall stay."

"All winter, Master?"

"No, no! The sun is yet three hours in the sky. We will use it to scrape together as much as we can before fleeing the country."

Quickly he gave orders for Thomas to place the gifts in the cache and cover it, then gather collections of plants and animals in places he had seen. After the hunter had left, Steller ordered the boat crew to come back to the beach at sunset, and with that he moved off along the upper shore to examine new territory which he had not seen.

Seals, sharks, whales, and sea otters swam not far out in the water. As he strode along the beach, Steller saw red and black foxes. Ravens and magpies swooped over the shore.

Wildflowers and shrubs grew everywhere. Breaking trail away from the beach, he passed through patches of upland cranberry, whortleberry, and crowberry. He saw a strange raspberry and, although the fruits were not yet ripe, he tasted them, and quickly dug up several small plants in the hope of taking them back to Russia for transplanting.

"A berry so delicious," he said to himself, "must be introduced to the world."

Again he heard the raucous chattering he had heard before, and now a bird the like of which he had not seen anywhere, flew into view. It was a bright blue jay with a black crest.

"Hello there," he said. "What a handsome fellow you are."

He returned to the beach at sundown, stowed his collections in the jolly-boat, and climbed aboard. Thomas arrived from his hunting trip and, as the last dregs of sun-

Steller's blue jay

light drained from the clouded western sky, they rode back to the *St. Peter.*

Steller was sure now that there would be a dressing-down for his refusal to go back to the ship when ordered. But, to his great astonishment, Bering greeted him with a cup of chocolate.

"You had good hunting today?" the captain asked.

"I can't begin to tell you the things we saw and collected. It is as great a country as Kamchatka."

Khitrov reported that he had found a passage leading to good anchorage near the mainland.

"Did you see any Indians?" Steller asked.

"We found a hut made of hewn boards," Khitrov said. "It had a floor of timbers, and a fireplace in one corner."

"Did you see any of the people?"

"No, but someone had been there before we got there. Here are some of the things we found." He opened a sack and showed them a basket, a shovel, and a small stone with copper stains on it.

"We found shellfish," Khitrov continued, "and later saw a hut containing fish dried not many weeks ago."

Steller asked: "Did you see any tracks?"

"On the beach, yes. But the savages must have run away when they saw us coming."

"Then you saw nothing of them?"

"Nothing."

As Steller had feared, next morning the captain gave orders to depart. Monsoon winds would soon come in from the southwest, Bering said, exactly from the direction in which they must sail. Waxel suggested that they finish filling the water casks, of which about twenty were still empty, but Bering refused.

Thus at seven that morning—July 21, 1741—the sailors sprang into the rigging.

"Ready forward?" came the lieutenant's cry.

"Aye, aye, sir!"

"Ready aft?"

"Aye, aye, sir!"

On command, the canvas fell in rippling sheets from the mast heads to the deck. The yards were trimmed and the anchor weighed, and the *St. Peter* stood out to sea.

❧ 9 ❧

SHUMAGIN'S ISLAND

SUMMER goes quickly from Alaska, once July has begun to wane. The *St. Peter* now headed out to sea, bound for home. Dark clouds blew down upon her from the north, and the wind rose, and rain swept across the slippery deck.

Steller kept watch from the quarterdeck or from his Lookout. Or he stood at the taffrail, gazing back across the troubled sea where America had long since disappeared. What had the Indians been like? What was the smoke he had spied from the hilltop? What animals would he have found if he could have gone across to the mainland?

"Fear not," Plenisner consoled him, "as soon as she learns of our discovery, Empress Anna will send out another expedition at once. Then you can spend a whole winter in America."

Steller did not smile. To think that they had come all this distance for only one day on American soil!

"And there's been some trouble," Plenisner said.

"Trouble?"

"You've been so busy, we didn't want to tell you."

"What is it?"

"One of the men is sick."

"Who?"

"Shumagin, a sailor."

"What's wrong with him?"

"We don't know."

"Well, has the assistant surgeon seen him?"

"Yes. But he does not know what is wrong. The sailor grows sicker day by day. He will eat nothing and now is so weak he can move but little."

Steller jumped off the quarterdeck. "Come on," he said.

The steerage had a sour, musty smell. They found Shumagin in his berth. Steller held a lantern close to examine him.

"Shumagin," he said, softly.

The man did not speak. In the pale light of the lantern his face had a ghostly pallor and his sunken eyes looked like dark holes in a white canvas.

"How long has he been like this?" Steller asked.

Thomas replied that the man had been unable to walk since they had sighted the American coast.

"That has been almost a week."

"Yes, Master. We carried him once to the deck to let him see the land."

Steller ordered the sailor's trousers removed, and then bent to place his fingers against the legs. The man's flesh had become soft and limp and had lost its springiness. The legs were swollen.

"Hold the light closer," he said. "Here, now, to the face."

Shumagin drew back painfully from the light. "Listen to me," Steller said, bending near. "Can you open your mouth?"

Shumagin's eyes darted beyond the lamp, as if he were

trying to make out the dark forms in the steerage. He tried to lift his head but fell back, moaning slightly. Then he spread his lips, and with difficulty opened his jaws.

There were gasps now from Plenisner and Thomas and the others who had gathered to watch. All could see that the sailor's gums were badly swollen and that his teeth had become loose in their sockets.

"What's wrong with him?" Plenisner asked.

Steller eased Shumagin's head down on the bunk and took the lamp. He walked to the door of the steerage and paused to look back upon the dark and crowded quarters of the crewmen.

Then he said to Plenisner in a low voice: "A thousand headwinds could not do against us what this will do."

"Why?"

Steller handed the lantern to Thomas. "That man," he said, "has the scurvy."

On the morning of August 2nd, Steller wrote in his journal: "We found ourselves . . . only about three versts distant from a rather large and wooded island. The weather was unusually pleasant and warm, sunshiny, and absolutely calm. Towards noon a sea lion appeared near the ship and swam continuously around it for more than half an hour . . ."

It was the first time they had seen a sea lion. The animal was larger than a seal, with a thicker neck and short, coarse hair that was not nearly as beautiful as that of the fur seal. There were scars on its hide, souvenirs of summer battles.

From what he could see of it, Steller judged the animal to be ten feet in length and to weigh nearly a ton. Yet it swam gracefully, as if lord of the ocean. Perhaps

Steller's sea lion

on some distant rocky shore, many summers before, it had learned to swim by flopping into the sea with its mother, floundering a little, but finally mastering the turbulent surf.

Now it was an excellent swimmer. As Steller and the crew watched from the deck of the *St. Peter,* the sea lion dived for fish and for whatever crustaceans it could find in the shallow water.

"I shall call it *Leo marinus,*" Steller said, "lion of the sea."

Plenisner, as usual in such circumstances, busily sketched the animal from various angles. "Very well," he said, "but I wish your lion of the sea would hold still so I could draw him!"

After the sea lion was gone, Steller dropped a small hook and line into the water and within a short time caught two fishes that he had never seen before. They were some kind of sculpin, but not similar to those he had studied in the Academy of Sciences in St. Petersburg, and unlike any he had seen off the coasts of Kamchatka. He got out his journal at once and made a description of them while they were fresh, then preserved them in a bottle of spirits that he had brought along for such a purpose.

As evening drew nigh, the wind freshened. The crew sprang aloft and made sail again, whereupon the *St. Peter* swung around the island and passed out to sea in a westerly direction.

Again the clouds and rain closed in and it must have seemed that the decision to steer directly for Kamchatka had been made none too soon. Day after day, caravans of fog and drizzle crept ghost-like across the sea and blotted out the sun. Time and again the ship lay drenched with clammy dew.

Soundings, made regularly to test the nearness of land, revealed nothing at 90 fathoms.

Steadily the winds came from the west and southwest, directly athwart the ship's course. The vessel turned this way and that, but made little headway.

And all the time the days of summer were passing by.

Steller and Plenisner kept close watch across the wind-whipped sea. They saw many sea otters and fur seals. They saw more sea lions. They watched schools of dolphins leaping and plunging playfully through the water, often coming very close to the ship. Once a shoal of whales rolled sluggishly through the water, heaving with long-drawn breaths.

Driftwood and sea grass floating on the surface indicated that the ship was in the vicinity of land. At daybreak on the morning of August 29th all hands were on deck early. Off the starboard bow lay five islands.

The day was clear, with a light wind. Yushin lowered the jolly-boat and, with several men, went off in search of a good harbor. They found the bottom of the bay rocky and gravelly, and late in the day the *St. Peter* arrived at a suitable anchoring place. When darkness closed in at eight o'clock the anchor was dropped and Yushin and the sailors returned aboard.

That night, while preparations for landing were under way, Steller went down into the steerage. He talked briefly with Betge, the assistant surgeon. More than a dozen men had now collapsed from scurvy, their faces yellowed, their eyes sunken and staring. He moved from one to another, soothing as best he could, with a kind word here, a bit of hope there. The men moaned in pain, and the sound of it was painful for him as well. But he comforted the sick as well as he could, and went again on deck.

"Cheer up, my friend," Plenisner said, setting his lantern on the forecastle. "We are going ashore tomorrow."

"While so many are sick below," Steller said, "I cannot be cheerful."

"Did you see Shumagin?" Plenisner asked.

"Yes."

"How is he?"

Steller looked away in silence.

"Poor Nikita," Plenisner said, "he does not wish to die."

Steller said: "I found today that Bering is also sick. It is the scurvy. He spends most of his time in bed. He does not complain, and I who have been living in his very room did not know he was ill."

"We must do something," Plenisner said.

Steller was thoughtful. "There may be a way," he said.

"A way?"

"Yes. There have been experiments on certain plants. It is said that if men with scurvy eat fresh vegetables, they will be cured."

"But we have no fresh vegetables aboard. Nor any fruit."

"That is what is wrong, now, I think. But I have an idea."

"What is it?"

"Yon island, Friedrich. Tomorrow let us seek what plants are there. If we find the right ones, this scurvy may be battled."

At that moment Plenisner jolted upright and pointed off into the darkness. "Look," he murmured.

Steller turned quickly in the direction indicated. "Where?"

"Over there, on shore."

Steller peered into the darkness and suddenly saw that a large fire was burning, its glow reflecting in the water.

"A fire!" he shouted. Men, hearing the exclamation, came on deck and pointed excitedly toward shore. "The Indians!" Steller said. As far as he could judge, the fire lay about two and a half miles away, but he could see no sign of life around it.

Early next morning two boats were made ready for a landing. Into the longboat, in charge of Eselberg, went ten barrels to be filled with water. The other boat, the small yawl, was to be commanded by Khitrov, whose instructions were to go ashore where the fire had burned and search for the natives.

Bering, from his bed, gave explicit directions to Khitrov. "If you find the Americans," he said, "take care not to harm them in any way. Take gifts with you. Treat the people kindly."

Steller, Plenisner, and Thomas went ashore with Eselberg and the water party. Upon landing, Steller set out to find water, and soon did, some distance up from the beach—several springs that bubbled forth from the rocks. He knelt to taste the water. Excellent, was his conclusion. The sailors meantime had stopped at the first small pool and had started to fill the water casks.

"Esel, wait!" Steller called, climbing back down over the rocks and running along the beach to the boat. "Not here," he said. "This water is no good. I have found good springs, up there on the hill. Come."

"What is wrong with this water?" asked the navigator.

"Look at it," Steller said. "It is stagnant."

Eselberg scoffed. "What nonsense!"

"It is true. See how your pool rises and falls with the sea? It is as brackish as can be."

Eselberg bent down and scooped up a quantity of it in the palms of his hands, drinking heartily. "Bah," he said, wiping his mouth, "you are wrong, my boy. It is perfectly good water. Good enough for a thirsty man."

"But not for sick men."

"What do you mean?"

"The scurvy. Don't you understand? Those men on board must have fresh water. It must be pure, or they will get worse."

Yushin, who had also come ashore, strode up when he heard their voices to find out what the trouble was. When Steller told him, he said, "What is the matter with this water? The water is good; fill up with it." He ordered the sailors to fill the casks and to be quick about it.

There was nothing more to be said. With his black bag slung over his shoulder, Steller climbed over the rocks along the beach, Plenisner and Thomas following. He ordered Thomas to take a high point in view of the beach and the rest of the island, and give a signal if anything unusual happened. Then he and the artist made their way up a steep grassy slope and soon topped a rise overlooking the island.

Steller looked back. The sailors were filling the water casks and loading them aboard the boat. "Their beloved salty puddle," he murmured.

"There must be something we can do," Plenisner said.

Steller clenched his fist. "Men are dying aboard ship . . ." He stopped, his face red with anger.

Plenisner watched the flashing eyes, the angry scowl. "You are the doctor," he said.

"That's just it," Steller shot back. "And there is not a thing aboard ship for the scurvy. You saw the medicine chest. Plasters, ointments, oils, remedies for surgery. Enough for an army in battle."

"Can you give orders? About the water I mean? They will listen to you."

"They listen to nothing. They have ignored my pleas for help."

"But . . ."

"Friedrich, again and again we have tried. The officers do not listen. They think they have acquired all knowledge. And so what is left?"

"Say!" Plenisner brightened.

"What?"

"We can collect plants for everybody. Here, on the island. As you said."

"Do you know how much we would need? It would take barrels and barrels of leaves."

"It would?"

"And how long do you think they would last?"

Plenisner shrugged. "All right, you win. What now?"

"Just this: we will collect all we can, enough for the worst of the sick, and for Bering."

"How about us? Somebody's got to stay alive to take care of them."

Steller slapped him on the shoulder. "All right, my hungry friend. But first we've got to find these plants. Just any won't do."

As far as the eye could see, there were islands. Steller counted eight. Ducks, auklets, and cormorants flew overhead, winging their way above the bay and across the island. Gulls and guillemots clung to rocky ledges and perched on crags above the beach.

Steller drew a deep breath and let it out with a happy sigh. What a good day it was. The wind was only a breeze, the weather was clear, and scattered clouds dotted the blue Arctic sky.

As they made their way over the gray crags of the island, a black fox appeared from behind a small cluster of boulders and barked at them, coming so close that they could almost reach out and touch it. Walking on, they saw marmots leaping behind the rocks, and presently found what looked like tracks of wolves.

They were accosted by curious ravens that swooped in circles around them. Ptarmigans ran from rock to rock. Thrushes and snow buntings sang.

At last Steller gave a cry of joy. "Look! Whortleberries, crowberries! And over here—dock, watercress, gentian! These are what we seek. Come, Friedrich."

They ate as they collected. Steller stowed as many leaves as he could in his leather bag. Plenisner stuffed large bundles of plants in his pockets and inside his shirt.

"Ouch," he said, "that tickles!" They laughed; then suddenly Plenisner pointed behind them and said, "Look!"

A figure was running across the uneven terrain.

"It's Thomas," Steller said. "Something has happened."

Thomas arrived out of breath. "Master," he gasped, "they have brought the sailors ashore."

Steller grasped his shoulder. "Which sailors, Thomas?"

"The sick, Master. They have brought the sick ashore."

"Don't they know better than that? The sudden transition from the foul air of the ship to the pure air of the beach will be too much for them."

Thomas caught his breath. "Yes, Master. There is much confusion. One of the sailors is dying."

"Who?"

"Shumagin."

Steller picked up his leather bag. "Let's go!"

They found a disorderly scene at the beach. In canvas stretchers among the rocks lay the sickest of the sailors, unmoving. The water-collectors and the officers had gathered around one of the stretchers. On it was Shumagin.

Steller elbowed them aside and knelt beside him. Presently he rose slowly and turned toward Yushin.

"It is too late," he said.

Plenisner, coming up, asked: "Dead?" Then he stepped back, realizing the answer to his question.

Steller's eyes narrowed to slits as he faced Yushin. "I do not know who allowed the removal of these men from the ship, but I am giving you an order which is to be

obeyed without question. Return them to the ship immediately!"

When he himself reached the *St. Peter,* Steller strode
directly into Waxel's cabin. "Did you allow those sick
men to be taken ashore?"

Waxel, hunched over charts on a desk beside his bunk,
did not look up. Nor did he speak.

"Very well," Steller went on, "it does not matter.
Shumagin is dead."

With this Waxel looked up.

"We thought it would help them," he said.

"Who thought it would?" Steller asked.

"Betge and . . ."

"Betge knows better than that," Steller said, angrily,
"but he cannot speak in the face of your authority. Now
hear me, Lieutenant. The scurvy grows worse, and Shumagin will not be the last to die if we ignore the sick.
There is not a thing in the ship's wretched medicine chest
for the treatment of scurvy."

"What do you propose?" Waxel asked.

Steller waved his hand toward the island. "Out there,"
he said, "is the medicine." Opening his leather bag he
took out a handful of watercress. "There!"

Waxel's eyes showed a trace of grim amusement.
"Weeds?" he asked. "Men are dying on this ship and you
speak of weeds?"

"These are herbs that will cure the scurvy," Steller
said. "Eat these, and you will be saved from the awful
malady. If the sailors go without, they will all come down
with disease."

Waxel turned again to his charts. "The cure for scurvy
is not known," he said. "I would not trust the sailors with
your handful of weeds. They are not for experiment."

"All I ask," Steller pleaded, "is the assistance of several men, and some casks to be filled with fresh watercress and gentian. Let me try it. We have nothing to lose."

"All the casks are filled with water."

"Then something else. I do not care what it is. But I must collect enough for the sick. I must have a boat and some men . . ."

"We cannot spare a boat, Herr Steller. Master Khitrov has not returned from searching for the natives."

The next day Nikita Shumagin was buried on the beach, the first European to be buried in Alaska. As the members of the landing party gathered around, bareheaded, Steller said:

"That he may not have died in vain, O Lord, or suf-

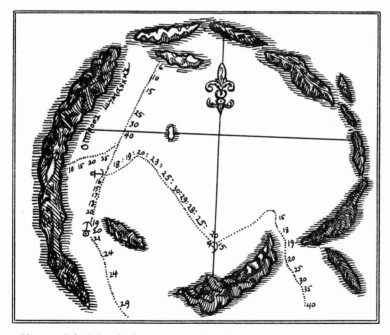

Shumagin's Island, drawn from sketch in log book of *St. Peter*

fered without cause, let us honor this simple sailor. Let us give his name to this island, for in no greater glory can a man spend his life than for God, for honor, and for beloved country. May his soul rest now and forever more. Amen."

That night aboard ship, Steller made a tea and served it to the captain along with some fresh watercress. The captain's face had become sallow and drawn and he could no longer rise from bed, but with the fresh herbs he seemed to improve, if only slightly.

A gale arose, and for two days no one could go ashore. When Khitrov returned on September 3rd he was called immediately into Bering's cabin to give a report of what he had seen.

"We found a good channel," he said, "sheltered from the winds."

Steller broke in: "Did you see the Indians?"

"We found a hut of hewn boards."

"Was anything in it?"

"An oven."

"What else?"

Khitrov brought forward a wooden basket, a crude shovel, a small stone with green copper stains on it, and a large round stone with a hole in it.

"But you saw none of the Americans?" Steller asked.

"None."

Khitrov turned and walked out on deck. "Up anchor, ye dogs of sailors," he shouted, after conferring with Waxel. "Hoist up those boats and loose those sails, or I'll cut up the lot of you and fling you to the fishes!" He strode up to the bow. The sailors were throwing overboard the line which was weighted with an ingot of lead. In this way they sounded the shallow bottom of the sea and helped guide the ship through the treacherous bay.

"Here," Khitrov said, wresting one of the lines from the hands of a sailor, "give me that. It's been a time since I've flung one of these over the side."

He swung the weight. It arched gracefully out over the bow of the ship and as it struck the water the line snapped out of Khitrov's hand. The lead weight plunged to the bottom of the bay. Khitrov's laughter was cut short as he stood with the severed rope in his hand.

The crewmen saw what had happened. They fell silent.

Plenisner, who had come on deck with Steller, whispered: "That big oaf. Why doesn't the crew laugh?"

Steller said: "They do not find it funny."

"Why?"

"It is bad luck to lose a weight at sea."

The sailors returned sullenly to work.

After making a little headway they anchored for the night. The next day was September 4th. The winds became southerly and light, not nearly strong enough to push the vessel out of the bay and safely away from the island cliffs. After trying to maneuver the *St. Peter,* and hoping the contrary and shifting winds would change, the officers decided to return to the place where they had spent the previous night.

They arrived at four o'clock in the afternoon and let go the small bower anchor in about twenty fathoms of water. Scarcely had this been done when a shout was heard from an island to the north.

"Look!" cried one of the sailors in the rigging. "Indians!"

10
INDIANS

THERE they were! Two Indians in small boats were paddling vigorously toward the *St. Peter.*

As they approached, Steller saw that their faces were brownish and somewhat flat, with flat noses. Their eyes were black, their lips prominent and upturned. Both had glossy black hair that hung down straight around their heads, nearly to their short necks and broad shoulders. Both wore whale-gut shirts neatly sewed together.

The boats in which they paddled were about twelve feet long, but very slim—two feet high and two feet wide at the most. Steller guessed that the frames were composed of sticks fastened at both ends and spread by crosspieces inside. The framework was covered with dark brown sealskins. To Steller they looked much like *baidarkas,* small Kamchadal boats.

Before they had drawn near the ship, both Indians commenced to speak loudly. The *St. Peter's* Koriak and Tchuktchi interpreters listened intently, then spread their hands in dismay. They could not understand a word.

Steller wondered if it might be a prayer or a welcoming ceremony, like those he had seen in Kamchatka and the Kurile Islands.

He climbed to a windlass and beckoned the natives toward the ship. Still talking, the Indians gestured in the direction of the island and made motions as if scooping something into their mouths.

"They're inviting us for a feast," Steller said.

"Well, lower the boats!" Plenisner exclaimed.

"Control your appetite," said Eselberg. "They may want *you* for the feast."

One of the Indians pulled out a stone and painted on his cheeks designs in the form of two pears. He then stuffed his nostrils with grass, and when that was done picked up a stick of spruce wood that had been painted red. On this he placed two falcon wings and a piece of what appeared to be whalebone and tied them fast. He held the object up for all aboard to see and then with a laugh threw it in the water toward the ship.

"What do you make of that?" Plenisner asked.

Eselberg answered: "A sign of sacrifice."

"Probably a sign of friendship," Steller said.

Waxel and Yushin tied two tobacco pipes and some glass beads to a section of board and tossed this into the water. The Alaskan picked it up, looked at it curiously, and paddled over to show it to his companion, who placed it on top of his kayak.

Now emboldened, the Alaskans rowed closer. One tied a falcon skin to a stick and ventured close enough to pass it up to the interpreter, receiving in turn a mirror and a piece of Chinese silk.

The natives now paddled back toward the island where other Indians were calling and shouting from shore.

Steller leaped from the windlass to the deck, and strode up to the officers. "Let's go after them," he said.

"They appear to be friendly," Waxel mused.

"Certainly," Steller said. "They have invited us for a feast. What better way is there to get acquainted and learn their habits?"

Khitrov sneered and said: "It is probably a trap. They are savages."

In the end it was agreed to follow them and Waxel, Steller, the Koriak interpreter, and nine sailors and soldiers made ready to go ashore.

For safety's sake they placed lances, sabers, and guns in the boat. These were hidden beneath canvas so as not to arouse the natives. Biscuits, brandy, and miscellaneous trinkets were also stored aboard. Then the boat was lowered, and the party rowed toward shore.

Steller could not remember when he had been more excited. It was the first time anyone had seen the Alaskan natives.

A rising wind had begun to whip up the waves; besides, the tide was coming in rapidly.

As they neared shore, they saw that the beach was very rocky, and was being pounded by a turmoil of waves and

Alaskan in

foam. Not even the best sailor could beach a longboat under those conditions.

By now there were nine Indians on shore and Steller could scarcely tell the men from the women, so much alike were their clothes. They wore loose shirts, some tied below the navel with a string. Two of them wore boots and trousers which appeared to be made of seal leather dyed reddish-brown.

Two others had long knives encased in sheaths that hung from their belts. Seeing these, Steller whispered that one should be obtained at any cost as an example of the workmanship of the people. One of the Americans drew out a knife and cut a sealskin pouch with it. Steller saw, to his great amazement, that the blade was fashioned of iron. Somewhere, somehow, the Alaskans had found a source of iron and learned to forge it into tools and weapons.

Because of the high waves, there was no way of beaching the big boat, though the natives had brought their small *baidarkas* ashore.

a *baidarka*

"You stay here," Steller said, "and I will go ashore."

"No," Waxel said, "we will test them first."

It was then decided that the interpreter and two other men would undress and swim ashore. They received a royal welcome. The Indians embraced them as if they were gods and soon led them arm in arm to a place where they had been seated. There, each Russian was given a piece of whale blubber. After this, some general and confused conversation followed, with neither side apparently understanding the other. The Indians pointed across the island frequently, as if beyond the rocks lay a village.

Meanwhile, several of the Alaskans, who had chosen to remain on the beach, beckoned to the rest of the Russians to swim ashore and be treated also.

One of the natives placed his boat in the water and paddled out through the breakers toward the longboat.

"Here he comes," said one of the soldiers. "Let us have some fun with him!"

They opened a jar of brandy, filled a cup, and passed it to the Alaskan.

"Be careful," Steller warned, "he is not used to that drink."

The soldiers laughed and downed a cup of the liquor to show how it was done. Following their example, the Indian raised the cup to his lips and drank.

"A-a-a-ach!" he blurted, belching forth a spume of liquid. He spat out as much as he could, then turned and paddled away in disgust.

"You see?" Steller said.

"Bah," said one of the soldiers, "it is good liquor."

"Perhaps to you. But you would not like to drink certain Kamchadal Indian delicacies I have seen—like rotten fish soup. You should have known better."

The wind had increased and the surf was becoming dangerous. Waxel cupped his hands to his mouth and called ashore for the men to return.

At this the Indians bestowed more gifts of red paint and whale blubber upon their visitors, and made wild gestures which Steller took to mean that they wanted the Russians to stay.

Waxel, eyeing the rising whitecaps on the bay, shouted again for the men to come aboard. At this the Indians seized the Russians on shore and held them by the arms. Two others grabbed the rope that was holding the longboat and began to haul it in toward shore.

"Leave be that rope, ye heathen savages!" Waxel shouted. "And let go those men!" The Indians, of course, gave no sign that they understood his words.

Loud shouts arose now from both sides.

The Indians were pulling the longboat closer and closer to shore, nearer the rocks where waves pounded thunderously.

"Fire the muskets!" Waxel shouted.

The soldiers complied. Three shots echoed across the choppy water.

Immediately the Alaskans fell to the ground as if struck by lightning. The Russians broke free and ran quickly to the beach, jumped into the water, and swam out to the longboat.

"Take to the oars!" Waxel shouted. "Heave, mates! Turn this boat around and pull out of here!"

The sailors bent to the oars and pulled mightily as spray whipped off the waves and stung their faces. Water had begun to collect in the bottom of the boat.

Suddenly the loose rope caught on some rocks and the longboat lurched sharply.

"We're stuck," a sailor shouted.

"Get the rope loose," said another.

The Indians were rising on shore and shouting angrily.

Steller leaped to the stern and leaned over to take the rope in hand and pull it from the rocks. But it was stuck fast.

"Cut it," Waxel shouted.

Steller drew a knife from his pocket and quickly severed the rope. With that the boat, under the oars of the soldiers and sailors, fairly leaped through the water. The natives made no effort to pursue them, and Steller thought it was because the storm had broken and winds of gale force were already plunging across the water.

Rowing with all their might, they returned to the *St. Peter* just as the wind began to swing dangerously around the mountains. Sail had been taken in on the *St. Peter* and dark clouds scudded across the bay. Only with great difficulty did they finally get the longboat aboard without damaging it.

All night rain lashed the ship, and part of the time sleet was driven fiercely on the icy winds. The ship strained at her cables, wallowing in the bay.

Next morning the deck lay covered with snow and the bow lines glimmered with icicles. The clouds had cleared at sunrise and a cold wind blew down from the northeast. Quickly the crew climbed aloft and unfurled the stiff frozen canvas. The *St. Peter* made sail again, and with favorable wind glided out of the bay into the open sea, leaving Shumagin's Island behind.

‹³ 11 ⅌

SHIPWRECK

DAY AFTER DAY the *St. Peter* fought against winds which came contrarily out of the west and southwest. The weather turned colder and flurries of sleet and snow fell. Sometimes there was a good wind, and the ship ran before it for hours without so much as bracing a yard or altering a sail, but those times were few.

On the afternoon of September 24th the darkest clouds seen on the whole voyage scudded low across the horizon.

"We're in for it now," said one of the sailors. "Ye never see clouds like that but what a storm's half on ye, and a big one, too, I'll tell!"

At first there was a topsail wind, but by nightfall it grew stronger and spray from the ocean waves blew straight across the deck of the *St. Peter.*

Steller, from his bunk in Bering's cabin, heard the ship being secured. "Lay aloft!" he could hear Khitrov shouting above the roar of the wind. "Loose the topsails!"

Steller rose and went on deck. A heavy and ugly sea had set in, and the wind was growing worse by the hour. He staggered to the rail and grasped a stanchion.

"All hands tumble up and take in sail," Waxel shouted. "Out, out, lubbers, aloft. Be quick at it or the ship'll break up—she'll break up on ye and then where'll ye be? Climb up! Climb up!"

Steller stood to windward as best he could, holding on by the backstays, and watching the sailors mount the rigging.

At length the stiff canvas was furled and the lieutenant ordered them below. Steller returned to the cabin.

Bering was quiet and resting, and Steller wondered if the old captain was even aware that the storm raged outside. After their stay in the Shumagin Islands, Steller had given Bering frequent doses of watercress and gentian, and the captain had managed to walk out on deck. He seemed noticeably improved. But he was weakened by age, and when the herbs gave out he had gotten worse. The scurvy was again upon him.

At midnight the storm struck in its fullest fury. As he lay in his bunk (sleep was out of the question), Steller listened to the deafening roar of the storm—a noise such as he had never heard before.

Tons of water poured over the ship. All night long rain and sleet hammered the deck. The *St. Peter* rolled and pitched and tossed, plunging through the water like a mad horse, throwing spray from every side. Steller feared that the vessel might ship a heavy sea, which would fairly ransack her and tear the masts away.

Next day the gale became worse, with hail and lightning, and no one could venture out on deck. But on the following day, storm or no storm, Steller knew he must see how the sick were getting along, and that meant walking across the deck to the forecastle and thence down into the steerage.

Wearing a leather coat and a canvas cap, he wrenched open the cabin door and struggled outside. Instantly he

was blinded by spray. The wind took his breath away.
Narrowing his eyes to slits he squinted along the deck
ahead. What a scene of chaos! The ship was plunging
dead into the highest waves, which rose like black, foam-
ing mountains. With a crash, water broke over the bows.
Tons of roiling sea pounded the forecastle. Every timber
shook. Every rope strained. Then the water washed aft
in the scuppers like a flood on a mighty river.

Steller leaped down the steps toward the mast. But the
wind caught him and flung him against the bulwarks. On
the slippery decks he almost lost his footing and nearly
slipped over the side of the ship into the sea.

He grabbed a stanchion and felt the vessel shudder as
she plunged into the next swell, as if slamming into a
solid cliff. The ship rolled sharply, tilting the deck to a
steep pitch of nearly 45 degrees. With a thundering crash,
a giant wave smashed into the bows and rushed toward
him. He flung his arms around the stanchion. Water
plunged over him, nearly ripping him loose.

As the sea subsided, he shook his head and spat out a
mouthful of salt water. From behind him came a shout:
"Herr Steller! Wait!"

It was Plenisner, crawling across the quarterdeck.

"Go back!" Steller shouted above the roar of the storm.
"Go back, Friedrich!"

"No, I want to go with you."

Another mighty wave broke over the bows and Steller
looked up to see a wall of water roaring toward him. With
a mighty leap he sprang up into the ropes, pulling himself
up on the forestay and holding on with a death-like grip
as the vessel buried itself in water.

He watched Plenisner tumble down the quarterdeck
steps just in time to get caught by the onrushing wave.

The artist was carried backwards and would have been thrown overboard had he not grasped a rope line and held on.

At that moment, however, Steller saw that Plenisner was caught in the ropes. The waves had twisted him around. Instantly Steller leaped from the rigging and, fighting the wind and spray, lunged up the quarterdeck steps and leaped onto the ropes.

"You're a miserable sailor," he shouted.

"Stop talking and let's get out of here," Plenisner cried.

Steller pulled desperately to untwist the ropes before the ship struck another wave.

The wind howled and screamed. Overhead, the spars snapped and cracked as if every bend would break them.

Suddenly Steller freed Plenisner's hands and the two of them dived down the steps and against the bulwarks. Another wave, with a deafening roar, crashed down around them.

They came up spitting and blinking and Steller said: "I told you to go back."

"I saw you from the cabin," Plenisner said.

"Well, why didn't you stay there?"

"I figured if you were going below you'd need help."

"Then come on."

Slipping and skidding, they ran along the gangway and plunged through the door of the steerage.

Inside, they found that things were not much better than on deck. Leaks had appeared in several places and some of the berths had become flooded. The men who could move had to huddle in whatever dry spot they could find.

The sick lay in corners that were least wet.

Steller and Plenisner knew that there was little they

could do. Beyond a few words of hope and comfort, there was nothing to say. The crewmen were too frightened to talk.

Day after day the storm drove on, without sign of let-up. In his pitching cabin Steller could do little more than lie on his bunk and think (trying not to listen to the storm), or doze fitfully, night and day. He made a cold tea for Bering and served it with hardtack. Sometimes he sat and watched the pounding waves through the stern windows, or made entries in his journal:

"Every moment we expected the destruction of our vessel," he wrote, "and no one could lie down, sit up, or stand. Nobody was able to remain at his post; we were drifting under the might of God whither the angry heavens willed to send us. Half of our crew lay sick and weak, the other half were of necessity able-bodied but quite crazed and maddened from the terrifying motion of the sea and ship. There was much praying, to be sure, but the curses piled up during ten years in Siberia prevented any response.

"Beyond the ship we could not see a fathom out into the ocean because we lay continuously buried among the cruel waves. Furthermore, we could neither cook nor have anything cold to eat except half-burnt biscuits, which were already beginning to run short. . . . Let no one imagine that our situation is here represented as too dangerous, let him rather believe that the most eloquent pen would have found itself too weak to describe our misery."

The sky remained cold and angry. The days grew shorter. Yushin, who normally took a reading of the ship's position from the sun every day at noon, was now completely unable to do so. The dark low clouds did not depart except for a few seconds at a time, much too briefly for readings.

Thus the *St. Peter* went on erratically, the sea flying over her, the bows plunging deep into the waters, the stern lifting high in the spray.

Day after day Yushin wrote in the log: "Heavy squalls, terrific storm." How the ship held together no one could guess.

On October 6th, Waxel reported to Bering that the brandy had given out.

Bering lay in bed. For days he had been unable to rise. "How is the water?" he asked.

Waxel replied: "We cannot go many more days. The water we have has turned foul and brackish. We have caught a little from the rain, but it quickly turns foul."

Steller said: "I give it to the sick, and they get sicker. Yet it is all we have."

"We are wandering," Waxel said. "We are far off course, and have drifted back toward America. We have tried to use the lower sails but cannot. The crew is exhausted. How much longer we can go on I do not know."

"We do not paint the picture more blackly than it is, Commander," Steller added. "If the vessel were to break up, we could not long survive in the small boats, not in this cold. And we do not know where we are."

Waxel said: "There is talk of returning to America for the winter."

"No." Bering's reply was firm.

"The wind is favorable for it."

"No. We shall make it, God give us courage."

"But we might find a harbor," Steller added, "and shelter."

"Avatcha cannot be far," Bering insisted. He had a fit of coughing, and when he had finished he dropped his head back and closed his eyes. "We will not fail," he said, quietly. "We must go on."

By the end of October, the big storm had abated. But the battered *St. Peter* and her exhausted crew were sailing past what would later be named Kiska Island, and swinging north of Attu Island out into the windswept Pacific. Fog and clouds obscured the sun. Storms came. Snow and sleet blew horizontally across the sea. High waves washed over the decks from both sides.

"Winter has arrived," Steller said to Plenisner, "and we are caught in it."

"Half of the men are terrified," Plenisner said, "and the others are too sick to be afraid."

"Yesterday we might have put up sails," Steller said, "but there was no one who could have climbed the spars."

"And what if they could? Who would furl the sails when the storm returns?"

"Only this morning," Steller said, "I saw the sailors take their posts at the tiller, led by others barely able to walk. Soon no one will be able to steer the vessel."

"Aye, already we are drifting."

Waxel no longer bore his gruff countenance, but went among the crewmen doing what he could. "Never despair, none of ye," he said. "With God's help and our strength— whatever is left of it—we will reach salvation. Pray and ye will see."

So they prayed, and as the days wore on, the *St. Peter* floated chip-like before the changing winds. Somehow Waxel kept the sailors on deck as long as they could work. But he knew they could not take much more.

In the log Yushin wrote: "I have such pains in my feet and hands, owing to the scurvy, that I can with difficulty stand my watch. 32 men on the sick list."

The scurvy grew worse. A grenadier died. Then a marine soldier. Then a Kamchatkan soldier. Then another marine. Then a naval cooper and another grenadier. By November, nine bodies had been lowered with simple ceremony into the sea. Then in a single day a drummer, a soldier, and a cadet succumbed to scurvy. And more lay waiting.

"I am altogether exhausted from scurvy," Yushin wrote in the log book, "and I stand my watch only because of extreme necessity."

The ship drifted on into the snow and winds and raging waves of the North Pacific. From time to time islands were seen. Then on the morning of November 4th a great land mass was sighted on the western horizon.

"Ahoy, mates, come see it! Come see it!"

"Land! La-a-and!"

"Hurrah!"

"Praise God!"

"It is our beloved Russia!"

"We are home again!"

"It is impossible to describe how great and extraordinary was the joy of everybody at this sight," Steller wrote. "The half-dead crawled up to see it, and all thanked God heartily for this great mercy."

In celebration, Steller made a cup of tea from some dried leaves for Bering.

"It is a great stretch of land, Captain."

Bering spoke slowly. "Can you tell where it is?"

"Everyone is sure that it is Kamchatka."

"What do you think?"

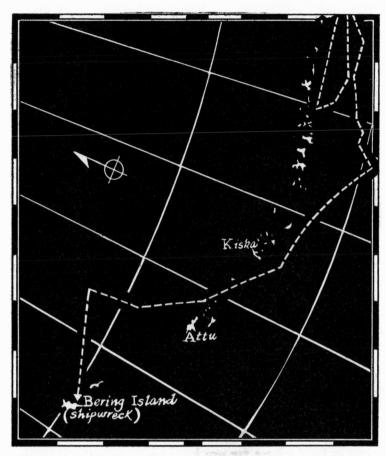

Route of the *St. Peter*—from Shumagin Islands to Bering Island

"I don't know. A headland perhaps."

"We will call a ship's council."

Presently the wind rose and a storm approached. They turned the *St. Peter* north, in order to keep safely away from land and not be blown onto shore.

Only a few seamen were now able to climb. The ropes were stiff with ice. Sleet had formed a crust around the rigging. The sailors had to work slowly, stopping to beat their hands upon the sails to keep from freezing. But it was no use. Before they had gotten all the sails furled, night came and the storm struck in all its fury.

The shrouds of the mainmast broke and swung free. A sail swept away on the wind, tearing and slatting itself to pieces.

"Lay to that sail," Khitrov shouted in a bull voice. "Furl it before it blows to tatters!"

But the sailors were now exhausted. None could climb into the rigging against the wind.

The morning of November 6th was raw and chilly, and there were snowflakes in the air. A ship's council was called on the quarterdeck. Everyone who could move came to it. Even Bering asked to be carried out to the deck. The petty officers were there. So was what remained of the crew.

"It is November," Waxel said. "The season is very late and the weather grows worse from day to day. Twelve of our number are dead. Thirty-four are totally disabled from the scurvy, and the rest are not fit for every kind of sea duty.

"Now taking all this into consideration we are of the mind not to go on down the coast to Avatcha. We propose to land where we are in order to save the ship and the men."

"You mean go ashore here?" Steller asked.

"It is better than being wrecked at sea," Waxel replied.

Khitrov spoke up: "Look at that mast—and the shrouds. This old ship will not hold together another league. We must land and make repairs."

"There is a bay over there," Waxel said. "A good bay. We have seen it through the glass. There must be a harbor."

Bering raised his hand. "We have already endured worse than we imagined. A little longer at sea should not hurt us."

"But the men," Waxel said. "Captain, the men are still dying."

"It is not far to Avatcha."

"We don't *know*."

Bering raised his arm slowly and pointed to the masts. "We can still use the foremast," he said, "and we yet have six casks of water, even if it is foul."

Khitrov stood. "Enough! Here is the paper. Let's sign the decision and make ready to land."

Lieutenant Ovtsin, one of the petty officers, spoke up. "How do we know this is Kamchatka?" he asked. "Have you thought of that? It may be an island, a big island."

"Are you questioning our reckoning, Lieutenant?" asked Khitrov.

"I will sign a decision in favor of landing only if you can prove that this is Kamchatka."

"You are insolent, Lieutenant."

"I only want to be sure. I am not an expert. If this is not Kamchatka, I stand with the captain in favor of sailing on."

"Get out!" Khitrov barked. "You scoundrel! Rascal! Get out!"

Lieutenant Ovtsin left.

"Now," Khitrov said, "if this is not Kamchatka, I'll let my head be cut off."

Bering asked the experts to voice their opinions. "Herr Steller?"

"I have never been consulted in anything from the beginning," Steller replied, "nor will my advice be taken if it does not agree with what is wanted. Master Khitrov has said before, if you recall, that I am not a sailor. Therefore, I would rather not say anything."

"Then," Waxel said, "will you sign a certificate describing the sickness of the crew?"

Steller shrugged. That would be his duty after all.

"Then be it decided," Waxel announced. "We will land."

The ship began to drift toward shore. By four o'clock in the afternoon they had come so close that Steller could see foxes playing on a gently curving, sandy beach. Behind the beach were several rows of dunes, covered with grass.

Behind the dunes Steller saw a broad grassy flat. This led to the base of the steep slopes of rounded mountains.

His heart rose at the sight. If it was Kamchatka, it was a section he had never seen.

Night began to fall and the sky was rapidly growing dark. The ship drifted closer, and Steller watched waves dashing against the rocks on the beach.

"Where are the officers?" he asked Bering. "There is no one on deck even trying to direct the ship. We are getting closer."

"They are exhausted from all the excitement," Bering said. "They are probably resting for the ordeal of landing."

"Well the time has come."

Bering sent word for the officers to take charge of the landing. Steller went on deck.

The breakers were now just ahead of the ship.

No one was on the bridge. In a moment Lieutenant Ovtsin appeared with three sailors.

"Quick," Steller said, "swing the weight."

Measurements were taken. Nine fathoms.

"We'll strike bottom," cried one of the sailors.

An anchor was dropped into the swirling waters.

By now night had come. The sky was clear and a moon was shining, bathing the sea and the turbulent waves in an eerie glow. The ship was being tossed by heavy swells.

There was a loud snap.

"The anchor cable has broken," Steller shouted. More men had come on deck. There was shouting and confusion.

"Let go another anchor," someone yelled.

They heard a grating noise of metal against metal. The second anchor fell with a splash.

In an instant the ship lurched again. There was another snap.

"We're done for," said a sailor. "The second anchor's gone!"

"The ship's running wild!"

Steller rushed to the side of the vessel. A few yards ahead lay a jagged reef. Waves pounded against the rocks. White foam spewed into the air.

Everywhere the men were in panic. "Oh God, our ship!" he heard someone cry.

"It is all over with us!" cried another.

"A disaster has befallen our ship!"

Steller ran across the deck. Neither Waxel nor Khitrov was anywhere in sight. Sailors were crawling in the gangway.

One of the men looked overboard. "Is the water salty?" he asked.

Steller shouted: "Would death in fresh water be more delightful?"

He ran forward to the Lookout. The rocks were nearly under the ship. He could hear the roar of the waves. In the moonlight the spray glinted like silver.

He clutched the Lookout chair and waited. A giant

wave rose under the *St. Peter* and the sailors shouted:
"This is it!"

"We're done for!"

Up, up the vessel rose, leaning on its side. A water cask
tipped over and rolled down into the gangway with a
crash.

The masts swayed. The yards creaked with the strain
and threatened to topple. A great surge from the sea drove
in behind the ship and pushed her forward. Steller, cling-
ing tightly, heard a scraping sound, somewhere deep
below.

Then, with a loud WHOO-OOSH! the wave subsided. The *St. Peter* fell. The breakers were quiet. The
reef was *behind* the ship.

"Did you see that?" Plenisner shouted, coming to the
Lookout. "A wave lifted us over the reef."

"It's a miracle," Steller said.

They leaped to the bulwarks and looked down. The
water was quiet. The ship was intact.

"We're in a lagoon," Steller exclaimed with joy.

৫৫ 12 ৯৯

DIGGING IN

WHEN MORNING came they found themselves in a shallow channel not far from the beach. The *St. Peter* was sitting at an odd angle in the water.

The day was clear and pleasant, and Steller breathed the air happily. "This weather can't last," he said to Plenisner. "The next storm will break the ship to pieces, or drive it out to sea."

Of the few able-bodied men left, Steller, Plenisner, and Thomas were the healthiest. They loaded aboard the longboat and, with Lieutenant Waxel and several of the sick men, rowed to shore.

A strange sight greeted them. Many sea otters came down to the beach and, as the boat neared, slipped into the sea and paddled away. Foxes ran back and forth on the sand, curious at the sight of the newcomers.

The boat was beached with difficulty and pulled up on the dunes.

"Solid land!" Plenisner exclaimed. "I'd almost forgotten what it was like."

Mountains—smooth and barren except for a mat of dried grass—rose from the flat just back of the beach. From the heights a stream of clear, wholesome water tumbled down over the black rocks and poured into the sea.

They drank their fill. Then Steller said: "Friedrich, you take the gun and hunt. I thought I saw some partridges running up on yon ridge. We need fresh meat for the sick, and we need it quickly. Thomas, come with me."

Steller and the hunter left the beach and climbed along the little stream.

"Here," Steller said when they came to a flat space alongside the stream, "this is the place for ship's camp. That dune over there protects us from the sea. The mountains protect us from behind. We will build here."

"It is a good place," said Thomas.

"And look here," Steller said, walking over to a terrace near the stream. "See these depressions in the sand? They will be good places to build huts. Go tell Lieutenant Waxel to examine this spot and see if he agrees. Tell him I have gone on up the slope looking for anti-scurvy plants. Then take your gun and walk along the beach. See what you can find for supper."

With that, Steller struck off across the grassy flat and headed inland.

The wind blew against his face. He felt good. He remembered *Robinson Crusoe*. Now it seemed that he was like Crusoe, except that he had a different job to do. There were sick and dying men on the *St. Peter,* and he had to find fresh vegetables. That would be difficult. It was November; already there were patches of snow in the shadows. Later there would be more. Not many plants grew at this time of year.

Yet hopefully he climbed on, up the steep slopes, across rocky flats, through stream gullies. He poked into crevices and found a few fresh leaves, protected from the winds and still green. He lifted boulders along the stream and found hidden herbs that looked like nasturtiums. He found brooklime, and watercress.

As evening came, he returned to the beach, carrying a bundle of greens. Also, his pockets were bulging with them. He noticed that Lieutenant Waxel was very pale.

"What is the matter, Lieutenant?"

"It is nothing," Waxel said. "I'm just a little dizzy."

"You are not well."

"I'm all right. I'm taking the boat back to the *St. Peter*. Are you coming?"

"Wait, I'll make you a tea."

"No, I'm all right."

"Come now, Lieutenant, I'm the doctor on shore. It will take only a moment."

They boiled some water and Steller made a rich fresh tea from the herbs. He handed a cupful to Waxel. "See if this doesn't make you feel better," he said.

He took some cups from the longboat and passed more tea to the sick men who were lying on canvas near the fire.

"This is good," Waxel said.

"Do you feel better now?" Steller asked.

"Perhaps."

Plenisner returned with half a dozen ptarmigans. Steller handed them to Waxel. "Take these aboard," he said, "and make a dish for the captain. Take some greens, too, and prepare a salad for him. Give him fresh water. He is very sick. Give some also to as many of the sick men as you can. We will stay on shore tonight."

After Waxel departed, Thomas returned carrying some partridges and sea otters.

What a delicious meal the little group ashore had that

night. They sat around the fire and drank a hot soup in which pieces of partridge meat had been boiled.

One of the sick men said: "The Lord sent you to heal us, Herr Steller. The Lord bless you!"

"Praise God that we are still alive," Steller said. "I pray that the men on the *St. Paul* have fared as well."

"I wonder what happened to them," Plenisner said, rising. "We may never know."

He left the fire and gathered some pieces of driftwood to build a hut with. When the poles were thrust into the sand, he covered them with an old sail and under this makeshift shelter the little group slept that night—with the moon shining in the cold sky and the sea washing up on the beach nearby.

The next days were busy ones. Men came ashore, carrying what supplies they could, and Steller directed the gathering of driftwood and the building of huts. At first the work went slowly. Even the able-bodied men were weak from exhaustion. The weather was cold and damp. Yet dugouts were cleared, driftwood erected for walls and rafters, and the new huts covered with sail cloth.

A large, square pit, with a canvas roof, was dug for the sick, who were brought ashore as rapidly as work and space permitted. Some were in a very advanced stage of scurvy. Their faces were yellow, their feet swollen, their teeth loose. Their mouths and gums were so enlarged and sore that they could hardly eat.

Steller, with the help of the assistant surgeon, Betge, did the best he could to comfort them. He covered them and kept them warm. He made meat soup and served vegetable tea. But too often the change from the foul air of the ship to the fresh air of the shore was too much.

Within the first few days after landing, eleven more members of the expedition had died.

The old navigator, Eselberg, was carried ashore. He had grown so weak that he could scarcely talk. Steller gave him tea and meat. But it was too late. The old man had reached a point of no return. Within a few days he, too, was gone.

Steller felt very sad. Eselberg had been his friend, had talked to him many hours about the sea, had told of early voyages, had helped him whenever there were disagreements with the officers.

To Steller it was as if his dearest friend had moved away, never to return.

Mourning was brief. The dead were promptly buried. For the survivors, life had to go on.

And life—morning, noon, and night—meant foxes. From the very first day they landed, they had been set upon by Arctic foxes. Steller could not imagine where so many had come from. The camp was constantly filled with them. Efforts to beat them off with clubs did little good. They came right back. Great numbers were killed, but more took their place. They barked and yipped and snapped at everyone's heels; they slashed with their sharp teeth at the sick and the dead, and stole everything that could be dragged away.

The most puzzling thing about them, Steller thought, was that they were so tame. Then, suddenly, he said to himself: "Tame? That means they have never seen men before. They have no reason to be afraid. If that's true, and there have never been men here, then we must be on an island. Not the mainland at all, where native tribes live, but an island never before visited by human beings! Is it really possible?"

Arctic foxes

He did not have time to think about it. More sick were arriving on shore. When the time came to move the captain-commander, special precautions had to be taken. Bering was securely covered for the boat trip and then was carried on a stretcher to a hut that had been prepared for him.

Snow had fallen the night before and the ground was slippery with slush. Steller directed every movement of the bearers, then made Bering as comfortable as possible. He prepared a bowl of soup made from sea otter meat and brought it to the commander.

"How do you feel?" he asked. "Tell me the truth."

Bering ate the soup heartily. "It is not I you must worry about," he said. "I will not be here long."

"As soon as you . . ."

"No, my son, you must not waste your energy on a worthless old man. My work is done. Tell me, what have you learned? Where are we?"

"I do not know, Commander."

"Are we not on Kamchatka? You know the country well."

"It does not look to me like Kamchatka. The foxes are too tame. I never in Kamchatka saw animals so unafraid of men. This must be an island."

"An island?" The commander raised his head a little. "But where? We know of no islands in this vicinity."

"The only thing I can say, Commander, is that we are not far from Russia—perhaps just off the coast."

"Do this for me. Tell Constable Roselius to take two men and follow the shore in a northerly direction to determine whether this land is some island or a part of Kamchatka."

"Yes, sir."

"Tell him if we are truly on Kamchatka soil he must keep going until he finds an inhabited place. There he will tell what has happened and send aid to us at once."

"I'll tell him. I will go with him."

"No. You are too valuable, my boy. We need you here."

The captain finished his soup. "What about the ship?" he asked.

"They want to bring it ashore," Steller said. "At high tide."

"Good. Good. If this is an island, the ship is our only chance of getting back to Russia."

He lay his head down and closed his eyes. Steller started to leave.

"Wait . . ."

"Yes, sir?" Steller knelt beside him.

The captain's voice was almost a whisper. "How are my men?" he asked.

"You must not worry, sir."

"Tell me."

"The scurvy has been bad for us."

"How many have died? Tell me, my son. I want to hear it from you."

Steller paused, trying to look away. Then slowly he recounted the names of those who had died.

Bering closed his eyes again. "The rest must live," he said. "You must bring them all back to health."

"I'll try, Commander," Steller said.

By November 15, 1741, all the sick men had been brought into camp. Waxel, the last to arrive, had to be carried ashore. He had become so ill that he could not walk, and Steller feared for his life.

Exploring parties had gone out across the mountains but had not found any connection with Kamchatka. Constable Roselius returned, weak and exhausted. He had walked thirty miles from camp, he reported, but had been unable to go any farther. He could not say whether this was the Russian mainland or an island.

The huts, built five in a row, were nearly finished. They were cold and damp, Steller knew, and unhealthy places in which to live. But at least they afforded some protection from the open weather.

Steller spent most of his waking hours in the barracks where the sick were crowded together. The other huts each held several men. In Steller's there were, besides himself and Plenisner, the assistant surgeon, the constable, and the midshipman.

"I like it," Plenisner said, laughing. "I go to sleep at night imagining that I am deep in a feather bed in St. Petersburg. And it works. I dream of all the gay lights and the parties and the feasts."

"Tonight," the constable said, "take me with you."

Not long after the huts had been completed, Steller and his companions were visited by Khitrov. The fleetmaster was weak from scurvy. His voice no longer had the deep, domineering tone that had become his trademark.

"What is it?" Steller asked.

"The crew," Khitrov said, in a frightened voice.

"What about them?"

"They are no longer civil. They have become ill-tempered. Today they talked back to me as if they had no respect for an officer."

"Isn't that what you expected?" Plenisner asked.

"What do you mean?"

"Listen to me," Steller said. "For all we know, we may be shipwrecked on an island somewhere in the middle of the Arctic Sea. Half our crew is dead or dying and the others are so weak they may not survive the winter. Our ship is broken to pieces and our supplies are nearly gone. How do you expect to give orders and have them obeyed under those circumstances?"

"Well I . . . I . . ."

"We are no longer officers and crew and expedition, do you understand that, Master Khitrov?"

"Yes, but . . ."

"Out here we are men. Plain, ordinary men struggling for our lives against great odds. We may not make it. We may never get back to Russia. Have you thought of that?"

"Of course."

"Then think it over again. You can no longer order these men about. It will be better for you to treat them with respect. Help them. Work with them. Be kind to them. Do I make this clear?"

For a moment Khitrov did not answer. He hung his head. Then he said: "You have built a very good hut here."

"Well, what do you mean by that?"

"Let me stay with you."

"Here?"

"Yes, please, I beg of you. The men do not leave me in peace. They threaten me, and reproach me constantly."

Plenisner laughed. "Oh, ho! Is this the great Master Khitrov who knew the sea so well? Begging! Come, come, Master. It is time you learned to get along with your shipmates. Now you have to live with them—man to man —and you don't like it."

Khitrov turned to Steller. "Please," he begged, "for God's sake."

Steller said: "If it were my decision, I would welcome you. I hold no grudge. But as you can see, we are five in here already. There is no room. It is as simple as that."

Steller found little time to write in his journal. But he did manage to make a few entries. "We now began," he wrote, "to regard many things as treasures to which formerly we had paid little or no attention, such as axes, knives, awls, needles, thread, shoe twine, shoes, shirts, socks, sticks, strings, and similar things which in former days many of us would not have stooped to pick up."

He kept up the sagging spirits of the sick—and the well, too. He reminded them that there was still very definite hope of returning to Asia. "We encouraged one another not to lose heart but with the greatest possible cheerfulness and earnestness to work for our own benefit as well as for the welfare of the others and by our exertions to support loyally their strength and undertakings."

One day, when he felt he could stop collecting herbs and caring for the sick for a while, Steller went on a hunting trip with Thomas.

They hiked southeast along the coast, in the direction of a steep point of land that jutted out over the shore. Beyond this the sandy beach ended and they no longer had easy walking. The shore became narrow and stony. It was fringed by a partly submerged rock ridge parallel to land and separated from it by a narrow channel of shallow water.

The surface of this ridge was furrowed, like a freshly plowed field, but the water of the rising tide now was coming in over it.

Suddenly Steller stopped, putting his hands on Thomas's arm.

"What is it, Master?"

"There it is again," Steller said.

"Sir?"

"Look beyond the reef."

Something was moving in the water. Something big. He could not tell what it was because most of it was submerged.

"It is some kind of a fish," Thomas said. "We have seen it swimming offshore from camp. It must be a big fish."

"No," Steller said, "it's not a fish."

"A whale, maybe?"

The huge creature had a black back. It looked like an overturned boat moving about in the surf. Every few minutes a snout in front of the animal emerged for a moment and drew in a gasp of air which sounded like a horse snorting.

"It is not a whale," Steller replied. "Since we landed on this island I've seen a number of these animals offshore. It is not a seal—or a sea lion."

"Master, maybe it is a sea monster!"

"Shush, Thomas, there are no such things."

"Then I don't understand."

"If only we could catch one alive and get a good look at it! Thomas, in all your years in Kamchatka, did you ever see anything like this?"

"No, Master."

"Are you sure?"

"Yes, sir."

Steller scratched his head. "Thomas," he said, "before we leave this island I must have a look at that animal. We must get one on shore!"

"But why, Master?"

"It is a sea cow, Thomas."

"A what?"

On the morning of December 8th a cossack reached into Steller's dugout and shook him.

"Master Steller! Master Steller! The commander is calling for you."

Steller groped his way through the darkness to the commander's tent. Inside, a candle was burning. Bering lay with blankets pulled about his neck, and on his wrinkled, haggard face was a peaceful expression. The old man opened his eyes slowly and smiled.

Steller said: "Commander . . ."

"I'm . . . glad you've . . . come," the old man said.

"I want you to know . . . my heart goes with . . . the men. You must tell them that . . ."

"Commander, please."

In the flickering light, the captain's smile was warm. His eyes sparkled. His gray hair touched the side of his face.

"I . . . have delivered my men and my ship . . . to this island, wherever it is, whatever it may be. My only wish is that . . . the ship may sail again . . . to carry you and all the rest back home . . . to our beloved Russia."

He closed his eyes, and his voice became a whisper.

"May God go with you from here . . ."

For a long moment the hut was quiet. In the distance the waves were washing onto the beach with a soft murmuring sound. In the tiny dugout, the only movement was the flickering candlelight and the silent shadows.

The old man was dead.

❧ 13 ❧

WINTER

A ND THUS has passed from earth, as nameless men have done before him, our brave and illustrious commander. It is his last mission."

They stood beside the grave, not far from Steller's hut. Everyone who could walk or crawl came there and, bareheaded in the raw December wind, paid homage to the old commander. Steller lifted his voice above the wind.

"He was the greatest navigator Russia ever had. He was our first great discoverer. Above all, he was a kind and gentle man, a man for whom we all held deep respect. And he in turn died with the welfare of his men on his lips.

"We give him here a simple grave. Yet we pay the highest tribute to his goodness and to his greatness, and by these shall he be remembered. For as we lay to rest our beloved captain, we enshrine him in our hearts forever. May God rest his soul."

As the wind-driven snow had battered the ship at sea, so did strong gales sweep off the ocean and blow across the little camp. Day by day the survivors settled into a routine of cooking, hunting, gathering wood, and tending the sick.

Steller said to Waxel: "You're improving, Lieutenant.
You'll be walking soon."

"I have to," Waxel replied. "Now that I'm in command . . ."

"Now, now," Steller interrupted, "the rest of us are
taking care of things."

"But the men . . ."

"I'll admit it looks a little black for us. There have
been more deaths, and will yet be some I fear. And winter
is full upon us. But at least we are alive."

"Thank Providence for that," Waxel said. "We must
keep our hopes up. Every man should strive to enjoy life
and make as much as he can out of our prison home."

"They will," Steller said. "Now you must rest. You
have worked too hard already."

One night a blizzard raged across the island, and the
little huts were nearly buried in snow. The next morning
Steller poked his head outside. Looking down the snow-
covered beach, he said to the others in the hut: "Do you
know what day this is?"

"Who cares?" came a grumbled reply.

"It's Christmas!" Steller said.

"Merry Christmas, one and all!" Plenisner said. "Now
let's go back to sleep."

"Awake, my merry friends," Steller said. "Today we
must have a cake."

Plenisner sat upright in bed. "A cake?"

"Of course. What is Christmas without a cake?"

"Just where do you propose to get one?"

Steller laughed. "I will bake one."

"Here?"

"Where else?"

"We don't even have an oven."

"We don't need one."

"Where will you get the flour? In case you don't know it, the flour in the ship has been lying hard-pressed in leather sacks for three years and is now impregnated with salt water."

"It will still bake, won't it?"

"Well, I guess so. But it tastes like gunpowder."

"Very well. Do not consult your taste when you eat it. Friedrich, these men have subsisted on the meat of seals and sea otters and ptarmigans for weeks now. They've been huddling together in the cold and wet of their huts so long that they are almost too cramped to move. Their close comrades have died. In the face of all this we must cheer them up in every way we can. We haven't much, but we must try. A change will do them good."

"All right, I'm ready. Let's try it."

They dug some hard chunks of flour from the hold of the ship, made small cakes from it, dipped them in seal fat and fried them in a frying pan secured from the ship's galley.

These they took, with a pot of tea, to the barracks of the sick and there ate and drank merrily.

"Ach," Plenisner said, "it *does* taste like gunpowder. But, then, it is pretty good in spite of that."

They sang Christmas carols and folk songs and then proposed toasts to the Empress, to Waxel, to Steller—and to their eventual deliverance from this place.

Soon every hut was singing. And there was laughter in the little dugouts.

"You did it," Plenisner said to Steller that night. "You gave them a merry Christmas!"

The day after Christmas a party of scouts returned to camp with proof that the expedition was shipwrecked on an island. The scouts had walked entirely around the island, starting in an easterly direction. They also reported that they had found cast up on shore such things as ships' rudders and bottoms of fish barrels.

"That proves it," Steller said. "We are just off Kamchatka."

The news, however, did not please the men.

"We thought we were *in* Kamchatka," one of the patients told Steller. "We thought rescue would be soon."

"Yes," said another. "We have only a broken ship. We'll never get off this island."

"There is no one to come after us."

"We are lost."

"We will all die here."

"Stop it!" Steller scowled at them. "We shall not escape if you are all of that opinion. Now we shall certainly perish."

"Herr Steller, what do you mean?"

"I mean that if you keep talking that way and keep resigning yourself to a terrible fate, it will surely come to pass."

"But there is no hope."

"We're alive, aren't we?" Steller asked. "We'll get to Kamchatka if we have to swim there! Trust Providence on it. And yourselves. The first thing is to get well. And then, who knows, we may soon be settling into a deep feather bed on our return to civilization."

"Oh," said one of the sailors, "I've been so long on this cold ground I don't even remember what a soft bed feels like."

"We've eaten so much sea otter," said another, "we've forgotten what good food tastes like."

"Be patient," Steller said. "Soon the seals will be coming. Then we'll eat! And in spring the berries will be growing. All you have to do is look at the bright side of things."

But as winter lingered bitterly on, the men lay cooped inside their dugouts while snow fell and the wind whistled outside.

Then the gambling with cards began.

"I was afraid of that," Steller told Plenisner.

"Well," the artist said, "there isn't much else for them to do."

"But it is worse than the scurvy. First they play for money. Then when they lose all their money they go out and kill sea otters for the skins and throw away the flesh. You wait and see. We will soon have to go many miles down the shore to find sea otters for food."

"I suppose so. This morning all I could hear on approaching one dugout was 'Stepan won two hundred rubles yesterday,' or 'Dmitri has twenty skins now,' or 'Ivan lost everything last night.' It becomes a disease with them."

"Exactly," Steller replied. "Pretty soon they will begin stealing from one another, and we'll have quarrels."

"Why don't the officers put a stop to it?"

"The officers are gambling, too."

Whenever anyone did get outside he was plagued by the foxes. In front of each house stood several barrels, which were used as storehouses to keep food safe from them. Scaffolds, or wooden platforms, were erected so that clothes could be hung out of reach. There was no room for extra clothes in the dugouts, and if anything was left on the ground outside, it would be torn to pieces or carried away by the foxes.

Steller was amazed by their clever ways. "They

crowded into our dwellings by day and by night," he wrote, "and stole everything that they could carry away, including articles that were of no use to them, like knives, sticks, bags, shoes, socks, caps, and so forth. . . . However well we might bury something and weight it down with stones, they not only found it but, like human beings, pushed the stones away with their shoulders. . . . If we cached something up in the air on a post they undermined the post so that it had to fall down, or one of them climbed up it like a monkey or a cat and threw down the object with incredible skill and cunning.

"They observed all that we did and accompanied us on whatever project we undertook. . . . At night when we camped in the open they pulled the nightcaps and the gloves from under our heads and the sea otter covers and skins from under our bodies. When we lay on the sea otters which had just been killed . . . they ate away from under us the meat and the entrails from the carcass. We therefore always slept with clubs in hand so that when they waked us we could drive them away."

In spite of the foxes, the situation began slowly to improve. One day late in January Steller said to Waxel: "The scurvy is over. The rest of the men will recover."

The lieutenant, who was himself rapidly improving, asked: "How many have died?"

Steller said: "Thirty-one."

"God help us! Almost half the expedition."

"Yes."

"And our companion ship, the *St. Paul?* Did she get to America? Did she return to Avatcha?"

"We will have to ask Captain Chirikov when we see him again."

"*If* we see him again," Waxel corrected.

One morning the weather turned pleasant and sun-shiny. Steller, Plenisner, and Thomas left camp and struck out across the mountains for the south side of the island. There they would find sea otters and could bring meat back to camp.

From the highest mountain, which rose nearly 2,000 feet in the sky, they looked around. The island consisted of bare cliffs and mountains which, though separated by valleys, seemed like a single mass of rock. There was not a tree anywhere, save thickets of small willows in protected places.

The ocean could be seen in both directions but Steller could not determine how far the island extended to the north or south. He guessed that the island must be nearly sixty miles long. Far in the distance, out to sea, were other, smaller islands, and because of the clearness of the day, mountains could be seen toward the northwest.

Were those mountains part of the mainland? Steller wondered.

Following a crystal-clear stream, they passed numerous waterfalls. In one place water fell step by step over a rock slope that looked like a wide stairway.

At sundown they made camp near a cliff, and soon had a fire from sticks of birch and alder shrubs that grew along the stream.

After a supper of brooklime and roast partridge, they rolled up in their blankets by the fire. But this was only a signal for the inevitable foxes to move in closer.

As Steller put it: "They sniffed at our nostrils to see whether we were dead or alive; if one held one's breath they even nipped our noses and were about to bite."

Towards midnight a violent northwest wind arose. Heavy snow began swirling in the air. The wind became

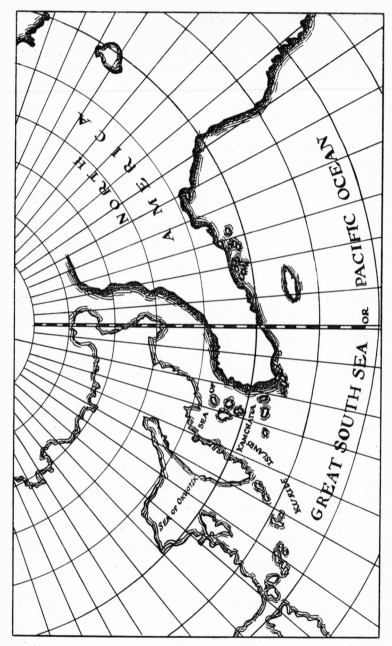

From a 1758 map of North Pacific region, showing erratic route of Bering's expedition

so strong that the fire blew away in a shower of sparks. In the darkness they could see nothing, but could feel the driving snowflakes against their cheeks.

"We'd better get out of here," Plenisner said.

"Let's stay where we are," Steller shouted above the wind. "If we get lost from each other in this blizzard it's the end of us."

All night long the wind howled and snow swept into the little camp. Plenisner stood up and walked around and around, though the wind several times nearly blew him over. Thomas bundled up in his sea otter skins and rolled up in the snow. Steller sat near him and tried to get a few moments' sleep.

The next thing he knew, Thomas and Plenisner were tugging at his shoulder.

"Wake up, Master, it's daylight."

Steller shook his head and looked around. He was covered with snow. The day was dark, and black clouds swept low over the mountains.

"Have I slept all night?" he asked.

"Aye," Plenisner said. "How any of us could sleep I don't know."

For hours in the blinding snow they climbed slowly up the stream valley, seeking a refuge. At last they came upon a wide and spacious cave.

Foxes had taken refuge there and were soon routed out. Thomas went back out into the storm and dug some wood from under the snow. After drying it as much as possible, they made a small fire. Fortunately there was a natural chimney near the back of the cave. Through this the smoke escaped.

In a little while the storm ended, and for three days

they hunted in the vicinity of the cave. Each night they tried to keep the foxes from pulling off their caps and socks. When finally the snow had blown from the slopes and melted sufficiently, they returned to camp.

Another party of hunters had been caught in the same storm with less success. They returned to camp so stiff from the cold that they could scarcely move. They were almost completely out of their minds and unable to speak.

One man was totally blinded from the glare of the snow, and remained so for more than a week. Another was discovered wandering aimlessly on the beach, knowing neither where he was nor what he was doing. He had been lying in a stream all night and his clothing was frozen solid. His hands and feet were so severely frozen that Steller feared he might lose them but, luckily, he recovered without harm.

Blizzard after blizzard struck the little camp. It was now March, and there had been almost no fair days since December. Even now there was continuous fog and damp weather. Violent winds blew out of the north and raked the naked beach. One night six feet of snow fell. At other times steady rains poured for days, melting snow in the mountains and sending floods down the narrow valleys. Once the floodwaters rose so high that they spilled over the terrace on which the dugouts had been built. Water poured into the huts and everyone had to flee until the flood went down again.

With spring approaching and the men recovering, everyone began to think of leaving the island. But the *St. Peter* had been broken by storms and tossed on shore. What could be done with it? Could such a battered ship carry them to Kamchatka?

Since it was a naval vessel, regulations required that a sea council be held to decide what to do. The first question was how to float the ship.

"Let's put rollers under it," someone suggested, "and float it out to deep water."

Waxel asked: "Where would you get timber big enough to do that?"

Just then a party of sailors came to the council. "Lieutenant," one of them said, "we have dug down beside the ship as you instructed."

"How deep is she buried?"

"Sir, the *St. Peter* is in nine feet of sand."

"Nine feet?" Khitrov exclaimed. "That means we can't float it."

"Well, then," said another sailor, "why not dig a trench from the ship to the sea and float it out that way?"

"A trench?" Khitrov said. "Nine feet deep? The sand would keep falling in it. Every tide would fill it up again."

Waxel rose to his feet. "I say it is impossible to float the ship as it now sits. The bottom, the keel, and the sternpost are all damaged, and the rudder has long since been carried out to sea."

"Then how will we get back to Kamchatka?"

"Just a minute, Lieutenant!" It was the sailor Ovtsin.

"Yes?"

"I think the *St. Peter* can be floated from her present position," Ovtsin said.

"Oh, you do?"

"Yes, sir. She's not as bad off as she seems. The stem and sternpost can be repaired. We can make another rudder, even if we have to make it out of driftwood."

"How about anchors?" Khitrov asked. "There's not a single anchor left, and we have little hope of recovering the ones that were lost."

"We haven't tried," Ovtsin said.

"Bah," Khitrov snorted, "the rigging is broken. The shrouds are torn. The ropes cannot be depended upon."

"But some of the bad rigging could be repaired."

"How?"

"Ropes can be replaced. We still have spare rope that hasn't even been used."

"What about the crack?"

"What crack?"

"There is a crack crossways below waterline. The ship would sink to the bottom of the sea."

"The crack could be repaired."

"Impossible! I say the ship is unfit for service."

"I say it is not!"

Waxel held up his hand. "Very well. Ovtsin dissents. Everyone else, I presume, agrees that the *St. Peter* is unfit for sea duty. That means that she must be taken apart."

"Taken apart?" one of the sailors asked.

"Yes."

"But, begging your pardon, sir, she's a naval ship. She's in the service of Her Imperial Highness, the Empress. It would be a shame to take her to pieces. A shame, indeed."

Khitrov spoke up. "Do you want to spend another winter on this wretched island?"

"No." The sailor subsided.

Waxel went on: "It is our desire to take the *St. Peter* apart and make out of it some kind of small vessel."

"We have lost three carpenters to the scurvy, Lieutenant," a sailor reminded him.

"And we have three left," Waxel replied. "Everyone else is able to work and take instructions. We will proceed as follows: twelve men skilled with the axe will spend their entire time on the carpenter work. Mate Yushin will take charge of the hunting detail, and see that the camp is supplied with meat. With the exception of the officers and Adjunct Steller, everyone is to hunt and work in such a manner that when one party returns home from the hunt, it will have a day of rest in order to mend clothes and shoes. Then it will be assigned duties in the construction of the new ship."

"Agreed?" Khitrov asked.

There were shouts of "Yes! Yes!"

"Then," Waxel said, "with the help of Providence, we may soon escape from this island."

Steller's sea arch on Bering Island

⤳ 14 ⤵

THE WILD ISLAND

With the coming of spring, work on the new vessel began. Everyone who had been down with scurvy was now up and improving, thanks to the soups and teas and herbs that had been gathered and given by Steller.

Everything was taken out of the *St. Peter* and brought together in one place on the beach. Grindstones were dressed. Tools were cleaned. Knives were sharpened. A smithy was erected. Crowbars, wedges, and hammers were forged. Wood was gathered. Charcoal was made.

"Well," said Steller to Plenisner as they watched the activities on the beach, "now we can get something done for science."

"Aye," the artist said. "Look at that sun. I didn't think we'd ever see it again."

"We've had enough fog and rain to last a lifetime," Steller said. "Anyway, we must make haste to record the plants and animals of this island before we leave. How much paper do you have left?"

"Plenty. It's a little watersoaked, but plenty."

"Then come on. We've got work to do."

From then on the days were busy ones, for now numerous new birds were flying over, and the island was beginning to show some signs of green and of spring flowering.

Everywhere they went, little pink primulas thrust their delicate flowers into the warm spring air. Violets grew among the rocks. Golden rhododendron bloomed in the mountains. Buttercups broke out into gay-colored blossoms on the sand dunes near the sea. Cloudberry burst into flower in the marshes, and iris in the swamps.

During April the first fur seals arrived, and by the middle of June great swarms of them were coming from the south, forming a rookery on that side of the island.

Steller and Plenisner watched them in awe from a rocky crag above the colony.

"Look down there," Plenisner gasped. "As far as you can see—seals, seals, seals! I've never seen so many in my life. How many are there?"

Steller shook his head. "I will truthfully say that I cannot guess. They're countless. They cover the whole shore. And something else . . ."

"What?"

"This solves a great mystery."

"About what?"

"Where the seals go in summer. They have been seen off the coast of Kamchatka in spring, traveling north. But then they disappeared. And not until autumn were they seen again—on their way south."

"You mean you never knew where they spent the summer?"

"No. *This* is where they come. To this island. Let's go."

"Go where?"

"Down into the rookery."

"Among the seals?"

"Yes," Steller said, "and when one of the old bulls leaps toward you—step lively!"

Plenisner's face turned white. He swallowed hard as he followed Steller down the slope.

The rookery was a noisy place. And it was busy. There were many battles going on. Thousands of seals lay on the shore and across the rocky coast. They were divided into families, sometimes families composed of as many as 120 seals, with one father who snarled in anger whenever another male came near.

Some of the seal pups played together like children. They imitated their parents. They practiced fighting and throwing each other to the ground. When this happened a father would sometimes rise up with a growl and crawl over to separate the two little fighters. He would kiss the victor and lick him with his tongue. Then he tried play-

Fur seals

fully to throw the young pup to the ground. He must have been proud of his little son—a pup worthy of a brave father.

Steller and Plenisner erected a small hut, or "blind," on a rocky rise in the middle of the rookery. They spent six days in the hut, observing and recording every detail of life in the seal rookery.

Steller was most astounded by great battles between the bull seals. They often fought for an hour. "They duck their heads and strike back," he wrote in his journal as he watched from the blind, "and one tries to ward off the blows of the other. As long as they are evenly matched they strike only with their front flippers, but as soon as one gets the advantage of his adversary he tears him with his teeth and jaws, shakes him, and throws him down.

"Then the others, who have meantime been mere spectators, seeing this, hurry up to assist the weaker one, as if they were umpires in the fight. With their teeth they inflict wounds as large and cruel as if they were made with a saber. After a battle the first thing they do is to go into the water and bathe their bodies."

When Steller and Plenisner had finished their work in the sealing grounds they hiked up the coast in search of sea lions, which were much larger and fiercer than the seals, and without the soft, velvety fur (see picture, page 126).

"How terrible they are to look upon," he told Plenisner one day as, from a distance, they studied a herd of sea lions at the edge of the sea.

"Look at that big one, there," Plenisner said. "He's a beachmaster if I ever saw one. He sits up on that rock as if he owned the whole world."

"Yes. Remember the one we saw from the *St. Peter* just

after we left Alaska? They seem fierce, yet they are afraid of man. They have learned the pain they can receive from hunters' weapons." He rose and stepped forward.

"Where are you going?" Plenisner asked.

"Down to the colony. You'll see what I mean." He strode down the slope.

"Be careful," Plenisner said.

Steller had predicted correctly. As soon as the sea lions heard him coming and saw him leaping from rock to rock down the shore, they turned their great bulks around and rushed in headlong flight to the sea.

One old bull, his scarred hide a souvenir of bygone battles, tried to escape but found himself cornered in a cluster of rocks. As Steller approached he shook his head and let out a bellow of fear and rage. So doing, he turned and faced Steller squarely.

"Watch out!" Plenisner shouted from above.

It was too late. The sea lion cried out and with another roar jumped off the rocks straight toward Steller. The naturalist leaped to a series of ledges and pulled himself up just as the slashing beast crashed by. The giant bull bellowed again and fled into the sea.

"Whew!" Plenisner said when Steller returned. "I thought you were gone for good."

"Well," Steller said, "I'll have to confess that for a moment I thought so, too. The moral of that experience is: always have a cliff nearby to crawl upon! Nearly every animal fights when cornered."

They returned to camp to find that the building of the new ship had met with delays. These, Waxel said, were "due in part to the disagreeable atmospheric conditions . . . and in part to the poor health of the men and the great distance from the source of authority, which made it unsafe to hold them strictly to their work, and nothing could be done without the consent of all concerned."

Nevertheless, in fog and rain, the old *St. Peter* was slowly torn apart, and a new vessel began to take shape.

"We might be able to leave as early as August," Plenisner said.

"August!" Steller exclaimed. "We must hurry, Friedrich, if we are to finish all that is to be done before leaving here."

Day after day they climbed over the mountain slopes of the island, drawing, writing, studying. They waded through swamps. They explored the marshes. They hiked for days along the beaches and rocky shores and beneath the sheer cliffs that edged the sea.

Birds flew everywhere. A little brown wren slipped in and out among the rocks, singing in a canary-like voice. Flocks of sandpipers hunted food on shore. Ducks swam in the breakers. Enormous flocks of guillemots perched in cliff rookeries above the water. Elsewhere there were loons, and auks, and geese.

"Listen," Steller said one day, cupping his hand around his ear to catch the faint joyous notes of a distant song. "The skylark has returned."

Queerest, perhaps, of all the birds was one they had never before seen. It was an odd, ungainly cormorant, a bird that perched on rocks near the water. It was as large as a goose, and had white around its eyes.

"We ought to call it a spectacled cormorant," Steller said.

Spectacled cormorant

Somehow, Nature had endowed it with wings too small to carry its weight—so it could not fly. The hunters were thus able to get close to it with ease.

"You see," Steller told Plenisner as they watched a flock of the birds being carried back to camp by the hunters, "the flightless bird does not have a chance. He is tame. He trusts everybody."

Plenisner thought a moment. "Then that means . . ."

"Exactly," Steller said. "I predict that these birds will be extinct within a hundred years."

Now he and Plenisner were ready for a job bigger and more difficult than any they had tackled before.

"For days," Steller said, "we have watched the sea cows swimming around out there, but not one has been brought ashore."

"We must do something about that."

"Yes, but how?"

Soon he had his answer. The hunters, whose duty it was to supply the shipbuilders with food, were having an increasingly difficult time finding sea otters, seals, and other animals. Most of these had been frightened away. Hunting parties had to walk nearly twenty miles to find them, and then had to carry the meat all the way back to camp.

Yet all the time, swimming lazily offshore and munching nonchalantly on sea grass, were the sea cows.

"But are they good to eat?" the men had asked.

Steller answered: "I have read that it is so. They are supposed to taste like beef."

That was all they needed to know. One day the hunters succeeded in finding a sea cow swimming close to a rocky reef not far from camp. Quickly they captured it, and started to pull it in toward shore.

Not until then did they realize the enormous size and weight of the animal. For hours they tried to pull it into the shallows, over the rocks, and up on shore. They placed ropes around it and pulled with all their might. They pushed and shoved and tried every trick they knew. For a while it seemed as if they would not succeed, as if the giant creature would slip away from them and drift back out to sea.

More men came to help. More ropes were secured. Waxel and Steller shouted orders and instructions, and finally, with a powerful effort, they rolled the great beast up on shore.

Its thick, round-shouldered body tapered away to a broad tail, and its hide was like the bark of an old oak tree. Steller's first measurements showed it to be nearly thirty feet long.

Plenisner drew back and wiped his brow with a rag. "Whew!" he exclaimed. "I've never seen a creature that big."

Steller was equally amazed. "It must weigh four tons at least."

"Four tons! I think you ought to call it sea elephant instead of sea cow."

"Maybe we should. It is more closely related to elephants than cattle. Somewhere in its evolution, millions of years ago, its ancestors may have lived on land, as elephants do today. But then, as the years went by, more and more of them lived in the water. No one knows why, at least not yet. They just started swimming, I guess, and now they never return to land."

"Never?"

"Well, they may swim up rivers a little way, looking for grass, but they don't come out on shore."

"This one is out on shore," Plenisner said, surveying the dead animal. "Now that we've got it, what do we do with it?"

"Dissect it, of course."

"Dissect it? You mean cut it apart? You're joking!"

"No, Friedrich, certainly not."

"But why?"

"Because no one else in the world has ever seen a *northern* sea cow before. We have to describe it completely. There are other kinds of sea cows, different from this one, in the tropics. But we're the first people to discover this one—and he's four times as big as any other sea cow I ever read about. Is that enough of a reason?"

"Aye. I surrender. It's all for science. But I don't see how you're going to cut it open without tools like saws and axes and lifting chains."

"We'll make it, somehow. All we need is a little help."

"But the men are busy building the ship."

"I'll get some of them over here; you'll see."

Steller and Plenisner set about assembling books, paper, ink, and tools. Packs of foxes had gathered and were sniffing and slashing the carcass.

"We'll have to work fast," Steller said.

As a light fog drifted in from the sea and a drizzling rain began to fall, Steller returned to camp and went straight to his dugout. He took out his last supply of tobacco and with it succeeded in getting several of the sailors to help him.

He set at once to the task of carving the sea cow and dissecting out its various parts so that they could be examined and measured.

The foxes snarled and slashed, tearing away freshly

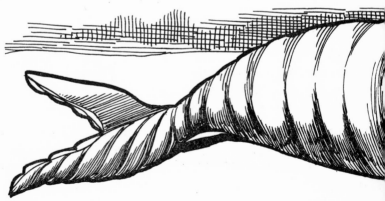

Northern sea cow. The man's figu

exposed meat, carrying off paper, even ripping the note-books while Steller was writing in them.

As carefully as possible, Steller and his helpers cut into the great beast. They penetrated a thick layer of fat that served to keep the animal warm in the ice-cold northern seas. Soon they reached the stomach, which measured six feet long and five feet wide and was, as Steller said, "so stuffed with food and seaweed that four strong men with a rope attached could scarcely move it from its place and with great effort drag it out."

After that, with a sailor's help, he managed to secure the sea cow's heart and carry it to some scales that had been improvised. It weighed over 36 pounds.

His assistant from the ship became tired and began to grumble about having to do this kind of work. "Not a single gut could I get out entire," Steller wrote, "nor unfold it, when gotten out."

Yet he scribbled notes and measurements as fast as possible, and Plenisner drew sketches of the parts as quickly as he could.

ves some idea of the animal's size

When darkness came they retired to camp, where the cooks had prepared a meal of sea cow steaks.

"M-m-m-m," Steller murmured, smacking his lips, "as tender and savory as beefsteak. And the melted fat is like oil of sweet almonds."

"A feast it is," Plenisner said. "We'll have sea cow steaks and sea calf cutlets from now on—even if I have to swim out and wrestle with these animals myself. Why this is food for a king!"

"It is certainly a change from seal meat and fox meat and flour soaked in gunpowder."

"Tell me," Plenisner said, "if this animal lives entirely in the sea and never comes on land, why does it not taste like fish?"

Steller's answer was simple. "It is not a fish."

"I know, I know. It is a mammal. But you'd think it would taste a little fishy."

"Perhaps that is because, like cows, it eats grass. Only here it is sea grass."

As summer came and the weather turned good, they captured more sea cows. Again and again Steller, with whatever help he could get, cut into them and studied every part of their anatomy. For hours he roamed the beaches and patrolled the barren reefs, watching the sea cows offshore and observing how they lived.

At night, by the light of a lamp that burned sea cow oil, he sat in a corner of his dugout and wrote what was to be the only description the world would ever have of the northern sea cow.

"This animal belongs practically to the sea, and is not amphibious," he wrote, "feeding upon vegetation about the shores of the sea and rivers . . . It is covered with a thick hide, . . . black, mangy, wrinkled, rough, hard, and tough . . ."

Its thick skin "seems given to the animal . . . to live continuously in rough and rugged places, and in the winter among the ice . . . It has to live, not in the depths of the sea as other animals and fishes, but it is always compelled in feeding to expose half of its body to the cold.

"The structure of the animal is totally unfitted for moving on dry land. Indeed, it happened that as the tide went out the waves receded from under one of the animals sound asleep and left him high and dry upon the shore; but he was helpless and unable to get away . . .

"These animals are fond of shallow sandy places along the seashore, but they like especially to live around the mouths of rivers and creeks, for they love fresh running water, and they always live in herds. They keep the young and the half-grown before them while they feed, but they are careful to surround them on the flank and rear and always to keep them in the middle of the herd. When the tide came in they came up so close to the shore that I often hunted them with my stick or lance, and sometimes even stroked their backs with my hand . . .

"Most commonly whole families live together in one community, the male with one grown female and their tender little offspring . . . The young are born at any time of year, but most frequently in autumn, as I judged from the new-born little ones that I saw about that time."

Steller had seen the animals eating constantly, "and because they are so greedy," he said, "they keep their heads always under water, without regard to life and safety . . . When they raise their noses above the water, as they do every four or five minutes, they blow out the air and a little water with a snort such as a horse makes in blowing his nose. As they feed they move first one foot and then the other, as cattle and sheep do when they graze, and thus with a gentle motion half swim and half walk. Half of the body—the back and sides—projects above the water. While they feed, the gulls are wont to perch upon their backs and to feast upon the vermin that infest their skin, in the same way as crows do upon the lice of hogs and sheep . . .

"When their stomachs are full some of them go to sleep flat on their backs, and go out a distance from the shore that they may not be left on the dry sand when the tide goes out. In winter they are often suffocated by the ice that floats about the shore and are cast upon the beach dead. This also happens when they get caught among the rocks and are dashed by the waves violently upon them. In the winter the animals become so thin that, besides the bones of the spine, all the ribs show . . ."

And in concluding, Steller said: "There is so large a number of these animals about this one island that they would suffice to support all the inhabitants of Kamchatka."

ᥱ 15 ᥰ

HOMEWARD BOUND

Wʜɪʟᴇ Steller was dissecting the sea cow, work rapidly neared completion on the new ship. Frame members were set up, the planking completed, the hull finished, and finally the calking applied.

At the same time, the water casks were repaired. Bread was baked. Meat was salted. All other provisions for the journey were made.

She was not a big ship—only 36 feet along the keel and 12 feet wide—but she was heavy enough so that a means of launching her into the sea had to be devised. Since there was no timber on the island, the launching ways had to be built of driftwood and of planks left over from the mother ship. All this was steadied and weighted with cannons.

At last, everything was ready. Prayers were held for a successful launching, and the little vessel was named, like her parent ship, after the Apostle *St. Peter.*

Shortly after noon on August 8, 1742, everyone gathered around the ship. The signal was given. Everyone shoved.

"Lay to 'er, mates!"

"She's moving!"

"Push, men, push!"

The ship moved down the ways.

"Keep at it! Shove! Shove!"

Suddenly there was a crash. The platform sagged, crumbled, collapsed. The ship faltered and stopped, sinking into the sand.

"She's stuck!"

Steller's heart sank. Groans of despair rose among the men. But Lieutenant Waxel quickly ordered the ship and platform lifted with jacks and some planks placed under her.

By the time this was done, the tide had gone out and the launching had to be postponed.

The next day, at high tide, everything was ready again. This time when they pushed, the new *St. Peter* slid smoothly into the water.

"Hurrah! Hurrah! The ship's afloat!"

After that they worked day and night. Masts were taken aboard and erected. Yards were rigged and sails hoisted. The rudder was put in place. One by one the barrels of water, sacks of flour, and crates of food were loaded aboard. The naval supplies were taken on. Finally the crewmen took their belongings onto the ship.

No one could take much baggage. Steller was limited to 360 pounds. This meant that he had to leave most of his collections, preserved skins, and equipment on the island. About all he could take were his notes and journals and a few of the most precious collections.

Others had to leave things behind also. For protection, a small, sturdy hut was built in which all the excess baggage was stored. Next year, perhaps, they could send a ship back to the island to recover this equipment.

They then left their huts for the last time, gladly, but

not without inner emotion. They had started as an expedition of 78 men. Now only 47 remained. In these simple dugouts they had been nursed to health. On this lonely beach they had lived nine months—and survived.

One last service of thanksgiving was held ashore, and a cross in memory of Captain Bering was erected on the old man's grave.

With that they went aboard for departure.

"When we were all together on the vessel," Steller noted, "we realized for the first time how cramped the quarters were and what a hard voyage it would be on that account; we were lying one on the other and crawled over each other."

With Waxel and Khitrov, he had a relatively comfortable place in the cabin. But the other men were "lying in the hold, which was crammed so full with water casks, supplies, and baggage that the people could hardly lie down between them and the deck. As the crew was divided into three watches, two places were assigned to three men. However, as the space was still too narrow, we began to throw into the sea pillows, bedding, and clothing, which had been brought from land. Meanwhile we watched the foxes on shore ransacking our dwellings with the greatest glee and activity and sharing among themselves what was left of fat and meat."

A west wind arose. The anchor was weighed, the sails dropped, and the sagging craft moved through the water, away from shore.

They were off at last! "This day," Steller recorded in his journal, "was enjoyed very much, as in the clear and pleasant weather we coasted along the island, on which we knew every mountain and valley which with much toil we had climbed so often in search of food or on some other reconnaissance and to which we had given names from various circumstances. Late in the evening we had come, God be praised, so far that we were opposite the extreme point of the island."

The next day, with favorable winds increasing, they made good time.

Steller watched the island growing smaller and smaller on the horizon.

"Would you like to go back?" Plenisner asked.

"Yes, I would, some day," Steller said. "We had a wretched time on that island. Yet I cannot help but think how things might have gone if we'd been forced to some less friendly shore."

"Aye," Plenisner agreed. "It could have been worse."

"We could have lost the ship entirely."

"We could have starved. Ah, but let us not consider what might have happened. Cheer up! We're alive! A bed awaits us in Avatcha. And news of the outside world. And after that—a trip back to St. Petersburg."

The island disappeared on the distant horizon.

Night came. The tiny *St. Peter,* now well out to sea, rose and fell with the gentle swells of the ocean. Her timbers creaked and strained, and the men slept as well as they could in their crowded quarters.

It was nearly midnight when a shout came up from the hold.

"We've sprung a leak! We're filling with water!"

Instantly the ship was in panic.

"Find the leak!"

"Save our ship!"

"God preserve us!"

Waxel ordered the pumps thrown into action.

"We can't, sir!"

"Why not?"

"The pumps are clogged."

Down in the hold the water was getting deeper and deeper.

"Shorten the sails!" Khitrov shouted.

"Move the baggage," Waxel ordered. "Find that leak!"

"Start bailing!" Yushin shouted. "Hurry!"

In the darkness the crewmen could scarcely see what they were doing. More lanterns were lighted. They could hear the gurgling of water as it poured into the hold. Frantically, kettles were passed below and the sailors began bailing.

"Bail!" Khitrov shouted. "Bail for your lives!"

"Throw over the ammunition!" Waxel ordered. "Get rid of the weight. Make the ship lighter or we'll sink to the bottom of the sea!"

The heavy cannon balls were quickly pitched over the side.

"Get the carpenters down here!"

One of the carpenters plunged into the hold and, by

Finding the leak

lamplight, groped about in the water, searching for the leak.

"Here it is," he said, suddenly.

"He's found it!" A great shout went up from the men aboard.

"God be praised!" said one.

"We're saved!" said another.

The leak was plugged. The sails were hoisted, and the little *St. Peter* once again sailed on through the darkness toward the Kamchatka mainland.

Great rejoicing filled Avatcha Bay when the battered remnants of the shipwrecked crew returned. The little ship sailed in with canvas flags flying, past Vaua lighthouse and into the harbor.

The commandant and the villagers met them at the wharf.

"We'd given you up for lost," the commandant shouted.

"We thought we *were* lost," Waxel said, shaking hands with him. "Glory to God that we're alive."

"Where in the world have you been? It's nearly a year and a half since you left here."

Quickly they described how they had lost the *St. Paul* in a storm, how they'd found America and explored the coast, how scurvy had plagued them, and how they had been shipwrecked and forced to spend the winter on a large and uninhabited island.

"Island?" the commandant boomed. "What island?"

"About five days' sail from here."

"You must be mistaken. There is no such island!"

Laughter filled the air. "You see?" Waxel said. "My men laugh. And well they should. They have explored every inch of that island."

"But we know of no island out there. What is the name of it?"

The officers looked at each other for a moment. Then Waxel turned to the commandant. "We have named it . . . Bering Island."

There was a long moment of silence. The commandant's eyes lowered.

"I see," he said. "I'm sorry."

After the unloading began, Waxel said to the commandant: "Tell us, what is the news from the outside?"

"The Empress has died."

"God rest her soul. Who rules the country now?"

"Elizabeth, youngest daughter of Peter the Great."

Steller asked: "What about Captain Chirikov and the *St. Paul?* Tell us. Did they reach America? Did they return? Where are they now?"

"Please, one question at a time! Yes, they returned last autumn and have already sailed for Okhotsk." The commandant then related the story that Captain Chirikov had told him. After the two ships became separated, the *St. Paul* searched briefly for the *St. Peter* but, not finding her, continued east.

On July 15, 1741, they arrived at the American coast, which was irregular and mountainous. Chirikov ordered the *St. Paul* to be taken as near land as possible. Sailors took soundings, hoping to find a shallow place. But as the vessel could not be taken close to shore, they never measured fewer than 70 fathoms, and that was too deep to anchor. The next day Chirikov gave orders to sail northward, and to look for a sheltered bay.

"Did they see any Indians?" Steller asked.

"Be patient, my friend! They did pass small islands on which were many sea lions. What Captain Chirikov wanted was to make a careful survey of the coastline, but his task was interrupted when tragedy struck."

"Tragedy? What happened?"

The commandant described how, on July 18th, Chirikov and the officers sent eleven men in a yawl to examine the coast. For a while the *St. Paul* followed the little boat as the men rowed along the rocky shore hunting for a suitable anchorage.

Soon the boat approached a bay and went in. The *St. Paul* hove to and waited. Night fell and the little boat did not return. At dawn the next day there was still no sign either of the boat or of the men who had been aboard it.

Chirikov moved the *St. Paul* in as close to the bay as he dared and fired signals. There was no answer.

"Was the weather good?" Waxel asked.

"Yes, for several days," the commandant replied.

"Then the men could have returned if they had been able."

"They could have."

"But they didn't?"

"For a few days," the commandant went on, "heavy rain fell and a fog set in. Then the men on the *St. Paul* saw a fire burning on shore."

"The lost men?" Steller asked.

"Chirikov thought so. He hadn't seen any Indians, so he thought the country was uninhabited. He felt certain that the fire had been built by his own men."

"Had it?"

"The men on the *St. Paul* fired a gun at intervals as a signal for the boat to come out, but no boat came. Instead, the fire on shore grew larger."

"Then the boat must have been damaged," Steller said, "and they were unable to leave the shore."

"Chirikov and his officers thought so, too."

"Then why wasn't another boat sent after them?"

"It was. The officers agreed in council to send two sailors with a carpenter and calker who could repair the boat on shore.

"Thus the second boat was sent ashore. On the following day, July 25th, two boats were seen coming out of the bay toward the ship, and the crewmen rejoiced that their comrades had been rescued and were returning. But soon they saw that these were not the boats from the *St. Paul.*"

"Not the boats from the *St. Paul?*" Waxel asked. "Then who were they?"

"Indians!" Steller exclaimed.

"Well," the commandant said, "they never came close enough for Chirikov to see their faces, but they did wave their hands and one of them shouted 'Agai, agai!' Then they turned and paddled toward land."

The commandant paused, as if his story had been completed and there was nothing more to be said.

"But what of the fifteen Russians ashore?" Steller asked.

The commandant replied slowly: "They were never heard from again."

With the loss of the little boats, the *St. Paul's* crew could no longer get ashore, even for water. So Chirikov and the other officers decided to return to Avatcha without further delay. On the way back, their food and water became low. They had to wring rainwater out of the sails and catch it in buckets that had been used to hold tar. Day after day they lived on nothing but mush and biscuit and butter, and even this had to be rationed. As a result of this diet, and because there was no chance of getting fresh vegetables from land, every man aboard became ill with scurvy.

"Chirikov told me," the commandant said, "that he was so sick he expected death at any moment. For three weeks he couldn't even come on deck.

"Six men died on the way back. Finally, on October 8, 1741, they sailed into Avatcha Bay and anchored.

"You should have heard them praise God for their deliverance," the commandant added.

By the following spring the men of the *St. Paul* had fully recovered. Once more they hoisted sail and this time headed east in search of the lost *St. Peter*. Although they sailed as far as Attu Island, they bypassed Bering Island entirely—thus missing a chance to rescue the beleaguered survivors of their shipwrecked sister vessel. When the search was over they turned back home and sailed for Russia.

Word had come for Plenisner to return to Okhotsk.

"Well, old friend," he said, shaking Steller's hand after a last service at the church on the hill. "This is where we part company. I wish you would come with me."

"No," Steller said, "my place is in Kamchatka. My work is not yet done."

"What will you do?"

"I must complete my survey of the natural history of the entire peninsula."

"Where will you go?"

"First to the Bolshaya River, I think. Next summer I will go farther north if I can—Kamchatka Post, Anadyrsk, up into the wild country."

They shook hands again. Steller remembered the good times and the bad times they had had together.

"We will meet again, Friedrich," he said. "God bless you."

"Aye," Plenisner replied, "we will indeed. Goodbye, my friend."

With that, the artist strode down the slope toward the ship.

"Master."

Steller turned. It was Thomas the Hunter.

"Are you ready, Master?"

Thomas was carrying a heavy pack to which snow-shoes were tied.

Steller picked up his pack and slipped the straps over his arms. Then he slung his leather collecting bag over his shoulder.

He paused a moment to look down at the bay. The little *St. Peter* lay at anchor, her worn and tattered sails rippling lightly in the autumn breeze.

Quietly he raised his hand in salute.

Then he turned toward the north. A trail led from the village across the mountains above the bay. Beyond, in the distance, rose the snow-capped volcanoes of Kamchatka.

Steller looked at Thomas and smiled.

"Let's go," he said.

❧ 16 ☙

THE LAST TRAIL

For almost two years Steller and Thomas explored the wild land of Kamchatka, from one end to the other. They lived on salmon from the rivers, berries and roots from trees and shrubs, bulbs from various herbs.

There were no horses, so they traveled thousands of miles by foot, climbing high mountain passes, crossing swamps, fording streams. Often they followed primitive trails, and sometimes stayed at native villages, learning the customs of the people.

In the Far North they went by dog team and sled across the ice and snow. And as always, night after night, Steller sat beside the campfire, writing in his journal about the things he had seen during each eventful day. We may imagine that often his mind turned back to the days on Kayak Island and Shumagin Island and Bering Island— places where so many scientific questions remained unanswered. How he must have hoped some day to return to those islands, and to see many others like them.

Meanwhile, back in St. Petersburg, Waxel and Chirikov had arrived with news of Bering's death and had made a full report of their journeys to the Governing Senate.

The Senate then decided that the Kamchatka Expedition had fulfilled its purpose and thereupon issued an imperial order to end further undertakings. A letter was sent to the Academy of Sciences asking for a report on what the professors, adjuncts, and other scientists belonging to the expedition had accomplished in conforming with their original instructions. The Senate also wanted to know whether it was still necessary for these scientists to remain in Siberia.

The Academy replied that no reports had been received for some time, and it was therefore not known how much work remained to be done. However, in view of the Senate's wishes to conclude the expedition, the Academy would order its members to finish their tasks as soon as possible and return home.

Consequently the official letter of recall was signed and dispatched to Steller on January 31, 1744, instructing him to return to St. Petersburg and report to the Academy. As he traveled across Siberia, the order read, he was to describe diligently and carefully everything met with pertaining to natural history. He would examine and describe new fishes, collect seeds of herbs and roots of shrubs, and preserve as many plants as possible for transplanting in St. Petersburg.

When he read this, Steller packed his belongings, sent his notes and collections ahead by mail, and started on the long trek home.

For nearly two years he traveled across Russia, stopping repeatedly to observe and to collect. Then one cold autumn day in Tobolsk, when he had traveled more than half the distance back toward St. Petersburg, he came down with a violent fever.

His friends begged him to stay in bed, to rest and

recuperate. They wanted him especially not to go out into the cold autumn snow. They were afraid his fever would get much worse.

But he was still young enough to be impetuous, and he was anxious to return to St. Petersburg. It had been eight years since he'd left. He wanted to begin cataloguing the collections he had sent there. He wanted to start writing about what he had discovered. Perhaps he would see Helen again. He wondered what she was doing. And Augustin. And his family. He would have to make a trip back to Windsheim.

So, with his fever growing worse, he crawled into his sledge. "Goodbye, my friends," he said, "I must be on my way."

The trip was made quickly for he had arranged to travel day and night, changing horses along the way. But he did not get far. On November 12, 1746, he arrived in the town of Tyumen, a city on the bank of the River Tura.

His fever was by then so severe that two naval surgeons, whom he had known in earlier days, rushed to his bedside.

Desperately they tried to reduce the fever and save him. But the rugged frame had passed beyond help.

Before the day ended, Georg Wilhelm Steller was dead.

When the news reached St. Petersburg and spread on to Europe, the world of science was shocked and sorrowed.

"I lament," said the great Swedish botanist Linnaeus, "and shall never cease to lament the loss to botanical science of Steller, who during his great journey traversed so many hitherto untrodden lands . . . O merciful God, that you have taken away such a man!"

Augustin was saddened and deeply disturbed. He had always been close to his brother. It had been more than twelve years since they had talked, since Augustin had predicted that Georg Wilhelm would find a way to go to Russia. There were so many things they could have talked about now—and so much he wanted to hear of the adventures of the expedition. And, as far as he knew, Georg Wilhelm had not learned that Papa Steller had died more than three years before. Perhaps it was better that he had never known.

The only solace for Augustin was the fact that inquiries about his famous brother were now coming in from all parts of Germany. As a result, Augustin wrote and published a short biography of his brother, and this remains today as the only personal record of the naturalist's early life.

As for Helen, she had long since returned from Moscow, where Steller had left her, to the gay pleasures and giddy society of St. Petersburg and, as history tells us, she seems to have forgotten that she had a husband so far away. It was as if now she was making up in frivolities for all the hardships of her early years with Dr. Messerschmidt.

History forgets—or does not know—how she felt when told of Steller's death. In a short while she was married again, and beyond that there is no record of her later years.

Friedrich Plenisner continued in government service and advanced to the rank of colonel. He became commander of Okhotsk. He supervised the building of a fort along the land route to Kamchatka and thus helped make travel safe against marauding natives. Under his leadership, parts of Kamchatka were investigated and explored, and further expeditions were sent along the northeast coast of Siberia. He returned to St. Petersburg finally, and died there in 1778—thirty-six years after he had said goodbye to Steller on the windswept coast of Kamchatka.

Waxel ultimately rose to the rank of captain-commander and was appointed to the office of intendant at the great Kronstadt naval station, near St. Petersburg. He died in 1762, at the age of sixty-one.

Yet of all the things that happened after the conclusion of the Kamchatka Expedition, perhaps the strangest story is that of the little makeshift vessel *St. Peter*. You would have imagined that such a little boat, put together under difficult conditions and after great hardships on Bering Island, would have been abandoned forever as unseaworthy. But not at all.

Ships were too valuable in those days, and the distinguished career of the little *St. Peter* was not yet over. The vessel was taken to sea again by hunters and was subsequently utilized on two expeditions back to Bering Island, one in 1747, and the other in 1750.

Three years later the *St. Peter* was one of three vessels that sailed from Okhotsk to Kamchatka and were wrecked there. For a long time the little ship drifted helplessly, with the rudder gone, and was finally washed up on the Kamchatka coast. Three men were thrown overboard, four were drowned, and four died of exposure after having reached the shore.

This, surely, was the end of the battered ship. Surely now it had served more gallantly and gone through more adventures than any other vessel. But no! It was repaired once more, and in 1754 made one last dangerous trip back to Okhotsk. There the illustrious little *St. Peter* was beached, and was never taken to sea again.

This, then, marked the end of one of the greatest sea adventures of all time. The crews of both the *St. Peter* and the *St. Paul* had opened up to the world a rich and fabulous land.

The extent of their discoveries, considering how scurvy raged through both ships and how the crewmen stayed on deck despite pain and exhaustion, remains a tribute to these hardy pioneers of the sea.

They established that De Gama Land was a myth and that America lay much more than "a few days' sail" from Kamchatka. Chirikov, commanding the *St. Paul,* discovered America at what is now Cape Addington, Alaska, and surveyed the rugged coast north of there. On the return voyage he found and charted the end of Alaska's great Kenai Peninsula, the Island of Four Mountains, and Adak and Agattu, as well as other islands.

Bering, in the *St. Peter,* charted Alaska from Mt. St. Elias to the Semidi and Shumagin Islands. He also saw Atka, Adak, Kiska, Buldir, and numerous other islands in the Aleutian chain. His was the first vessel in the Commander Islands where, on the island subsequently named for him, he died in 1741.

Both ships had penetrated the inhospitable and wholly unknown North Pacific Ocean, one of the most stormy regions on the face of the earth. This had proved that navigation of these ocean vastnesses, even in the bitterest winter weather, was possible. It was a "gateway" to Russian expansion on the North Pacific, and to eventual Russian ownership of the vast land that is now Alaska— today a part of the United States.

Steller, in spite of the limitations of the expedition, endured hardships beyond the capacity of an ordinary man, and for the first time in history, collected, studied, and

Discoveries made by *St. Paul*

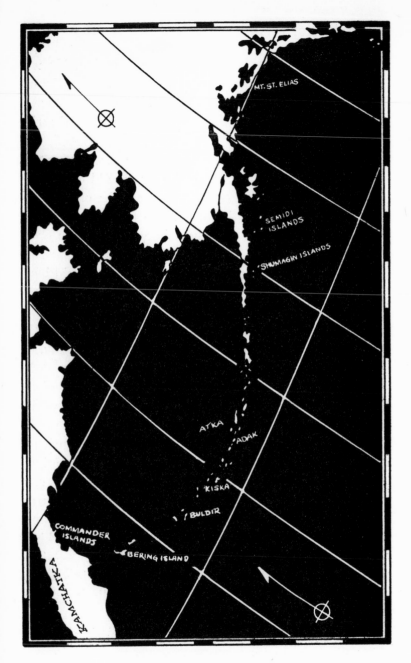

Discoveries made by *St. Peter*

described the plants and animals of the region. He was not only the first naturalist in Alaska but the first scientist to explore and describe any of the North Pacific Ocean north of Japan and California. His writings and descriptions are today priceless.

He was the only scientist ever to see that vast region in its natural, untouched state. To the world of science, he is the only eye-witness; his words are the only record of the land and sea and living things that existed before the hunters came and plundered its wildlife to the brink of destruction.

Steller was buried on a high bluff along the right bank of the River Tura, near the town where he died. As the years went by, the river slowly undercut its banks, and at length his remains were carried away to mingle with the creatures he loved so well and described so faithfully.

His death, at 37 years of age, came much too early. "For if weather, time, and place had favored my desire," he once said, "I should have enriched natural history with many curiosities . . ."

The truth is that in his brief, eventful life, he enriched the world with a treasury of discoveries and descriptions.

The northern sea cows, several of which he dissected on Bering Island, were so severely slaughtered by hunters that, a century later, there was not a single one left anywhere in the world. There were, and still are, other kinds of sea cows, or manatees. But the northern one is extinct. Steller was the only naturalist ever to see, dissect, and describe it. That is why it was named Steller's sea cow (*Rhytina stelleri*).

For more than a hundred years Steller's elaborate account of the fur seal, written largely from his blind in the midst of the colony on Bering Island, was the world's only complete and accurate description of that animal.

When his notes on the sea lion were finally printed, it was the world's first introduction to an animal that naturalists would later name Steller's sea lion (*Eumatopias stelleri*).

The spectacled cormorant was first described to the world by Steller. Within a hundred years it was hunted to extinction.

The bright blue bird that had so thrilled him in Alaska, and of which he collected the first specimen, was named Steller's jay (*Cyanocitta stelleri*). Happily, this race of birds did not become extinct, and Steller's jays are today commonly seen throughout the mountain forests of western North America.

Steller wrote in glowing tribute of the mountain peaks on the coast of Alaska. One of them, soaring ten thousand feet into the brilliant Arctic sky, is now named Mount Steller. Likewise, the highest mountain on Bering Island has been named Mount Steller.

And so the list goes on.

When the famed botanist, Linnaeus, chose the name *Stelleria* for a new group of plants, he asked: "Who has earned a greater or more precious glory for his name than he who undertakes journeys among the barbarians? If my appeal has any influence with you, I beg you to adopt the name."

Were Linnaeus alive today he would be pleased to find that, in all, Steller's name has been applied to an Alaskan heather, a blue jay, a duck, a sea eagle, a mollusk, three fishes, a sea cow, a sea lion, a sea cliff, and two mountains!

It is history's fitting tribute to an eighteenth-century Robinson Crusoe whose dreams of adventure came true.

FOR FURTHER READING

Andreyev, A. E., editor, *Russian Discoveries in the Pacific and in North America in the 18th and 19th Centuries,* 1952, J. W. Edwards, Ann Arbor, Mich.

Bancroft, Hubert Howe, *History of Alaska, 1730–1885; The Works of Hubert Howe Bancroft,* Volume XXXIII, 1886, A. L. Bancroft, San Francisco, Calif.

Brooks, Alfred H., *Blazing Alaska's Trails,* 1953, Caxton, Caldwell, Idaho.

Cahalane, Victor, *Mammals of North America,* 1947, Macmillan, New York, N. Y.

Coxe, William, *Account of the Russian Discoveries Between Asia and America,* 1803, Cadell and Davies, London.

Fisher, Raymond H., *The Russian Fur Trade, 1550–1700,* 1943, University of California Press, Berkeley, Calif.

Golder, F. A., *Russian Expansion on the Pacific, 1641– 1850,* 1914, Arthur H. Clark, Cleveland, Ohio.

———, *Bering's Voyages, Volume I, Log Books and Official Reports,* 1922, American Geographical Society, New York, N. Y.

———, *Bering's Voyages, Volume II, Steller's Journal of the Sea Voyage from Kamchatka to America and Re-*

turn on the Second Expedition, 1925, American Geographical Society, New York, N. Y.

Hrdlicka, Ales, *The Aleutian and Commander Islands and Their Inhabitants,* 1945, Wistar Institute of Anatomy & Biology, Philadelphia, Pa.

Jordan, David Starr, and others, *The Fur Seals and Furseal Islands of the North Pacific Ocean;* Part 3, 1899, Government Printing Office, Washington, D. C.

Lauridsen, Peter, *Vitus Bering: The Discoverer of Bering Strait; Russian Explorations, 1725–1743,* 1889, S. C. Griggs, Chicago, Ill.

McCracken, Harold, *Hunters of the Stormy Sea,* Doubleday, Garden City, N. Y.

Nordenskjold, N. O. G. and Mecking L., *The Geography of the Polar Regions,* 1950, American Geographical Society, New York, N. Y.

Rambaud, Alfred, *History of Russia, from the Earliest Times to 1880,* 1880, C. F. Jewett, Boston, Mass.

Stejneger, Leonhard, *Georg Wilhelm Steller, The Pioneer of Alaskan Natural History,* 1936, Harvard University Press, Cambridge, Mass.

Steller, Georg Wilhelm, *De Bestiis Marinis,* 1751, Akademiia nauk SSSR, Novi commentarii, 1751; see translation by Jordan, David Starr, *The Fur Seals and Fur-seal Islands,* Part 3, page 179, 1899, Government Printing Office, Washington, D. C.

INDEX

Academy of Sciences, 32, 38, 127;
Steller and, 38, 41, 45-50;
Museum in, 42;
Observatory of, 42;
instructions from, for Expedition, 49-50, 211
Adak Island, 215
Addington, Cape, 215
Admiralty, Imperial, *see under* Imperial
Agattu Island, 215
Alaska, sighted, 104-106;
attempts to land on, 107;
Bering and, 108-111, 119, 121-122, 130, 136;
Steller on land of, 112-120, 130-135;
exploration of, 113-117, 120, 132;
wildlife of, 113, 116, 119-122, 125-127, 132-135, 205;
natives of, 114-118, 121-122, 129, 136-144;
sick sailors brought to, 133-134;
Shumagin dies in, 134-136;

St. Paul and, 205-208;
discoveries made in, 215-219
Aleutian Islands, 215
American Geographical Society, 10
Anadyrsk, 208
Anatomy, 27
Angara River, 57
Animals, 17, 19, 50;
in Schlossbach Forest, 15, 22, 26;
of Siberia, 44, 59;
study of, 55;
on Bering Island, 185, 192;
of Alaska, 215, 218; *see also* under name of animal
Arctic Circle, 49
Aristotle, 19
Atka Island, 215
Attu Island, 151, 208
Auklets, 132
Auks, 190
Avatcha Bay, 154, 155;
expedition sails from, 67-78;
church and buildings at, 67-71, 90;
return to, 204-209

223

Bach, J. S., 17
Badgers, 18
Baidarka, 138, 141
Baltic Sea, 38
Barby, Duchy of, 19
Barguzin Bay, 59
Barguzin Mountains, 59-60
Barguzin River, 59
Baykal, Lake, 59, 64
Beavers, 76
Beech, 12
Bering Expedition, logbooks of,
    10; *see also* Kamchatka Ex-
    pedition
Bering Island, 10;
  sighted, 152-153;
  storms at, 153, 173, 178-181;
  landing on, 156-159;
  wildlife on, 159-161, 163-165,
    169-170, 176-181, 185-190,
    192-198;
  camp on, 160-200;
  sickness on, 161-177;
  foxes on, 163-165, 176-181,
    194-195;
  exploration of, 166, 169, 178,
    185-190, 196;
  Bering dies on, 170-172;
  Christmas on, 173-174;
  rebuilding of ship at, 182-185,
    189, 199-200;
  capture of sea cow on, 192-
    198;
  departure from, 199-204
Bering, Vitus, news of, 36;
  meets Steller, 65-67;
  in council, 83-87, 154-155;
  with Steller, 91, 100, 106-111,
    121-122, 146, 164-166;
  and scurvy, 128, 136;
  death of, 171;
  discoveries of, 215

Berckhan, Johann Christian,
  joins Steller, 57;
  in Irkutsk, 57-61;
  journeys to Okhotsk, 64-65;
  Steller says goodbye to, 68
Berlin, 35-37
Betge, Matthias, as assistant sur-
    geon, 72, 134;
  with Steller, 128, 162
Bible, 19, 24
Birch, dwarf, 60
Birch, silver, 54
Birds, 26, 42, 86, 185, 190, 219;
  see also under name of each
    bird
"Blind," 188, 218
Blizzards, 173, 180-181
Boar, wild, 18
Bolshaya River, 208
Botanical Gardens, *see under*
    Gardens
Botany, 30, 34
Brooklime, 161, 178
Buldir Island, 215
Buntings, snow, 132
Bustard, great, 19
Buttercups, 186

Cache, Indian, 115
Cantors, 16-17
Cape Addington, 215
Capercaillie, 14
Cape St. Elias, 107
Caribou, 113
Cathedral of St. Sophia, 48
Cedar, dwarf, 60
Chikachiev, Lieut., 88
Chinese New Year, 61
Chirikov, Captain, as command-
    er of *St. Paul,* 75;
  in Alaska, 205-207;

returns to Avatcha, 208;
returns to Russia, 208, 210;
discoveries of, 215
Chocolate, 110, 121
Christmas, 57, 173-174
Cloudberry, 186
Cochran, Dr. Doris M., 10
Commander Islands, 215;
see also Bering Island
Company Land, see De Gama
Land
Cormorant, 132;
spectacled, 190, 191, 219
Cossacks, 49, 54
Council, ship's, 83-87, 154-156,
182-184
Cranberry, 120
Crowberry, 120, 132
Crustaceans, 58, 126
Cyanocitta stelleri, 219

Dampier, William, 31, 36
Danzig, 36, 37, 41
Danilov, Aleksej, hired as guide,
56;
at Tomsk, 56-57;
at Irkutsk, 57-59, 61, 64;
in the Barguzin Mountains,
59-51;
journeys to Okhotsk, 64-65;
Steller says goodbye to, 68
Decker, Ivan, accompanies Steller as artist, 50, 55;
in Moscow, 51, 53;
journeys to Yeniseysk, 54-57;
leaves Steller, 57
Deer, 18, 60, 76
Defoe, Daniel, 32
De Lascy, Field Marshal, 37
DeLisle, Joseph Nicholas, 81
Dolphins, 127

Ducks, 132, 190, 219
Dutch East India Company, 81

Ekaterinburg, 56
Elbe River, 25
Elder, 60
Elizabeth, Empress, 205
Eselberg, navigator, 71;
with Steller, 77-78, 99-102,
130;
death of, 163
Eumatopias stelleri, 219

Feige, Doctor, 71
Finland, Gulf of, 38
Fir, 54
Fishes, 42, 58, 122, 126-127, 211,
219
Floods, 181
Four Mountains, Islands of, 215
Foxes, in Schlossbach Forest, 18;
on Kayak Island, 120;
on Bering Island, 163-165,
176-177, 181, 194-195, 201

Garden, botanical, at Witten-
berg, 27;
at St. Petersburg, 40-41
Geese, 190
Gentian, 132, 135, 146
Germany, 10, 15, 213
Gorse, prickly, 12
Great Northern Expedition,
see Kamchatka Expedition
(Second)
Grouse, hazel, 11, 12, 16
Guillemots, 132, 190
Gulf of Finland, 38

Gulliver's Travels, 31, 36
Gulls, 100, 101, 132;
    perched on sea cow, 198

Halle, city, 10, 29, 34;
    children's school at, 29-31;
    University of, 27, 29-34, 37,
    59, 72
Hamsters, 25
Handel, Friedrich, 17, 29
Harz Mountains, 31, 34
Hazel grouse, 11, 12, 16
Heather, Alaskan, 219
Heather, German, 12
Herons, 14
Huckleberry, 12

Imperial Admiralty, 49, 87
Imperial Senate, required to ap-
    prove Steller's trip, 47;
    correspondence of, 49
    orders from, 76;
    Waxel and Chirikov report
    to, 210;
    concludes Kamchatka Expe-
    dition, 211
Indians, evidence of, on Kayak
    Island, 113-117, 121-122;
    on Shumagin Islands, 136-
    144;
    met by Chirikov, 207-208
Insects, 30, 55, 61, 116
Iris, 186
Irkutsk, Steller arrives at, 57;
    description of, 58
    Steller prepares reports in, 61;
    departure from, 64
Iron, 141
Irtysh River, 56

Islands of Four Mountains, 215
Ivanovna, Anna, Empress, 75,
    205

Japan, prospect of going to, 34;
    limit of known land of, 49,
    218;
    survey of, 49;
    relation of, to De Gama Land,
    81, 84
Jay, Steller's 120, 121, 219
Jellyfish, 100
Jena, University of, 32
Justinus, 19

Kama River, 54
Kamchatka, Steller seeks infor-
    mation about, 44-45;
    conquest of, 49;
    location of, 67;
    Steller in, 68-78, 204-211;
    expedition leaves from, 78;
    wildlife of, 86, 186;
    relation of, to Bering Island,
    155, 165, 175, 204-205;
    expedition returns to, 204;
    investigations of, under Plenis-
    ner, 213-214
Kamchatka Expedition (First),
    49
Kamchatka Expedition
    (Second),
    news of, 36;
    plans for, 49, 50;
    crew of, 74;
    instructions to, 74-77;
    end of, 211;
    accomplishments of, 215
Kamchatka Post, 208

Kayak Island, description of, 107; attempts to approach, 107; landing on, 112-113; exploration of, 113-120; departure from, 122

Kazan, 54

Kenai Peninsula, 215

Khitrov, Fleet Master, 77, 136-137; in council, 84-86, 154-155, 182-184; with Steller, 97, 167-168

Kirensk, Fort, 64

Kiska Island, 151, 215

Koriak interpreter, 138, 140

Köthen, 32, 46

Kremlin, 51

Kronstadt, 39, 214

Kurile Islands, 138

Kyakhta, 61

Languages, 16, 19, 29, 30, 43

Lena River, 64

Leo marinus, 126

Lightning, 22

Linnaeus, Carl, 212, 219

Loons, 190

Luther, Martin, life of, 15; "Reformation" of, 15; celebrations in honor of, 15, 17-18; teaching, 21, 22; Steller visits tomb of, 24

Lutheranism, 15

Magpies, 120

Mammals, 42

Marmots, 132

Medicine, 28, 29, 30

Messerschmidt, Doctor, 44-45, 213

Minerals, 42, 44, 54, 61, 77

Mines, at Stollberg, 31

Monsoon winds, 122

Moscow, 51, 53

Mount St. Elias, 215

Mount Steller, 219

Music, 17, 29

Neva River, 40

New Year, Chinese, 61

Novgorod, 48

Okhotsk, city of, 66; Steller in, 66-67; voyages to, 205, 208, 214; Plenisner as commander of, 213

Okhotsk, Sea of, 68

Otter, 19, 76

Ovid, 19

Ovtsin, Lieut., in council, 155, 182-183; during shipwreck, 156

Pacific Ocean, 32, 34, 67; prospect of going to, 34, 51; exploration of, 49; Steller arrives at, 68; ships on, 79, 83, 96-98, 102-103, 123, 202; natural history of, 85-86, 100-101, 103, 125-127; storms on, 91-92, 127, 145-151; discoveries on, 215-218

Partridges, 15, 161, 162, 178

Peter the Great, 27, 41, 49, 205
Philosophers, ancient, 16
Philosophy, 29
Pine, 54, 114
Plants, 17, 50;
  of Schlossbach Forest, 22;
  study of, 27;
  collection of, 42, 211;
  of Siberia, 44, 54, 59, 61, 211;
  on Shumagin Islands, 131-
    132;
  on Bering Island, 160, 185;
  of Alaska, 218-219; *see also*
    under name of each plant
Plenisner, Friedrich, 70, 71;
  and Steller, aboard ship, 78,
    80-83, 88-89, 103-104, 128-
    129;
  on Shumagin Islands, 130-133;
  on Bering Island, 178-180,
    185-196;
  leaves Steller, 208-209;
  in later years, 213-214
Poland, 37
Politics, 30
Poppy, scarlet, 12, 13
Potentilla, 20
Primulas, 186
Ptarmigans, 132, 161, 174

Raspberry, 120
Ravens, 120, 132
"Reformation," 15
Religion, 15, 29, 30
Reindeer, 113
Rhododendron, 60, 186
Rhytina stelleri, 218
Robinson Crusoe, 32;
  inspires Steller, 34, 160;
  read aboard ship, 98
Rock ducks, 86

Roselius, Constable, 165, 166
Russia, Academy of Sciences of,
    32, 38, 41-50, 127, 211;
  Army of, 36-39, 93;
  Navy of, 78, 96;
  church of, 40;
  exploration of, 49;
  language of, 42, 49

St. Elias, Cape, 107
St. Elias, Mount, 215
St. Kilian, Church of, 16, 28
St. Paul, description of, 73;
  at sea, 79-92;
  loss of, 94-97;
  route of, 205-208, 216
St. Peter, description of, 73-74;
  from Kamchatka to Alaska,
    79-105;
  searches for *St. Paul*, 96-97;
  route of, 73, 108, 153, 180,
    217;
  wrecked, 156-158;
  rebuilt, 183-199;
  returns to Kamchatka, 201-
    204;
  final voyages of, 214
St. Petersburg, 36, 38, 39, 53,
    214;
  Steller's trip to, 37-39;
  Steller at, 40-51;
  departure from, 51;
  climate of, 56;
  Decker returns to, 57;
  Dr. Feige requests to be sent
    back to, 72;
  chocolate brought from, 110;
  Waxel and Chirikov return
    to, 210;
  Steller travels toward, 211-212
St. Sophia, Cathedral of, 48

Sables, 76
Sandpipers, 190
Science, 24, 29, 30
Schlossbach Forest, Steller's
    youth in, 11-16, 18, 20;
    natural history of, 11-15, 18-
    20;
    as an inspiration to Steller, 22,
    24, 59
School, children's, at Halle, 29-
    31
Sculpin, 127
Scurvy, discovered, 123-125;
    increases, 128;
    cure for, 129;
    on Bering Island, 162;
    deaths from, 152, 163, 177;
    end of, 177;
    on *St. Paul*, 208
Sea cow, Steller's, discovery of,
    169-170;
    dissection of, 192-196;
    description of, 196-198;
    used as food, 196
    history of, 218-219
Sea eagle, Steller's, 219
Sea grass, 100
Sea lion, description of, 125;
    Steller's observations of, 125-
    126, 188-189;
    seen by Chirikov, 205;
    named for Steller, 219
Sea oak, 86
Sea of Okhotsk, 68
Sea otters, seen from *St. Peter*,
    101, 103, 127;
    off Kayak Island, 120;
    on Bering Island, 159, 178,
    180;
    used as food, 161, 164, 174,
    175, 192;
    eaten by foxes, 177

Seals, seen from *St. Peter*, 101,
    103, 127;
    off Kayak Island, 120;
    on Bering Island, 175, 186-
    188;
    migration of, 186;
    description of, 187-188;
    Steller's observations of, from
    "blind," 188, 218-219;
    used as food, 192
Sealskins, 138, 141
Second Kamchatka Expedition,
    see Kamchatka Expedition
    (Second)
Semidi Islands, 215
Senate, Imperial, *see under*
    Imperial
Sharks, 120
Ship's council, 83-87, 154-156,
    182-184
Shipwreck, 38, 156-158, 214
Shumagin Islands, discovery of,
    128, 215;
    landing on, 129-130;
    exploration of, 131-133;
    natural history of, 132;
    death of Shumagin on, 133;
    burial of Shumagin on, 135-
    136;
    Indians of, 135-144;
    departure from, 144
Shumagin, Nikita, 124-125, 128;
    death of, 133;
    burial of, 135-136
Siberia, 34, 42, 48, 53;
    descriptions of, 43-45, 57, 59-
    60;
    explorations of, 49;
    Steller travels across, 53-67,
    211-212;
    natural history of, 54, 55, 57-
    60;

Siberia—*Cont.*
   towns and villages of, 54, 56,
     57-58, 64, 65, 211-212;
   rivers of, 54, 56, 57, 59, 64,
     212, 218
Skylark, 190
Snakes, 55
Snow buntings, 132
Spectacled cormorant, 190, 191,
   219
Stejneger, Leonhard, 10
Steller, Augustin, boyhood of,
   11-19;
   marriage of, 19;
   at Halle, 19;
   as an author, 20, 213;
   family of, 25, 26, 46;
   visited by Georg Wilhelm, 25-
     27, 32;
   learns of his brother's death,
     213
Steller, Georg Wilhelm, as musician, 17, 19;
   as minister, 17, 25, 28, 93;
   as teacher, 31, 34;
   as doctor, 37-38, 42, 58, 162;
   as naturalist, 17, 27-28, 30, 34,
     55-58, 60, 116, 185-198,
     215;
   information about, 9;
   journals of, 10;
   early days of, 11-23;
   mother of, 13, 21, 22, 23;
   father of, 16-17, 22, 23, 213;
   sisters and brothers of, 20;
   wife of, 51, 55, 212, 213;
   receives scholarship to Witten-
     berg, 21, 22, 28;
   leaves Windsheim, 23;
   at Wittenberg, 24-28;
   at Halle, 29-35;
   at Berlin, 35-37;

   at Danzig, 37-38;
   at St. Petersburg, 40-51;
   selected for expedition, 47;
   prepares for trip, 49-53;
   marriage of, 51;
   at Moscow, 51, 53;
   crosses Siberia, 54-65, 211-212;
   at Irkutsk, 57-64;
   meets Bering, 65;
   in Kamchatka, 68-78, 210-
     211;
   appointed physician, 72;
   aboard the *St. Peter*, 72-111,
     121-129, 144-159, 201-204;
   in Alaska, 104-151;
   argues with Bering, 108-111;
   shipwrecked, 156-158;
   on Bering Island, 156-202,
   recall of, 211;
   death of, 212;
   discoveries of, 218-219
Steller, Mama, 13-15, 21-23
Steller, Mount, 219
Steller, Papa, 22, 23;
   as cantor, 16-17;
   death of, 213
Stelleria, 219
Steller's Arch, 184
Steller's jay, 120, 121, 219
Stollberg mines, 31
Storms, on the Pacific Ocean,
   91-92, 96, 123, 145-152;
   at Shumagin Islands, 144;
   on Bering Island, 154, 172,
     178-181
Surgery, 28
Swift, Jonathan, 31

Tchuktchi interpreter, 138
Terns, 86
Theater, anatomical, 27

Theophan, Archbishop, 40;
  helps Steller, 40-41, 42-44;
  household of, 41-42;
  illness of, 46-48;
  death of, 48
Thomas the Hunter, 69-70;
  on Kayak Island, 112-121;
  on Bering Island, 169-170,
    178-181;
  in Kamchatka, 209-210
Thrushes, 132
Thunder, 22
Tobolsk, 56, 211
Tomsk, 56
Troika, 51, 53, 54, 57
Tura River, 212, 218
Tyra, Valley of, 31, 34
Tyumen, 212

United States National Museum,
    10
University of Halle, 27, 29-34,
    37, 59, 72
University of Jena, 32
University of Wittenberg, 21,
    24-28, 37

Vaua Lighthouse, 78
Vilyuchensk volcano, 68
Violets, 186
Volcano, 68, 78, 105
Volga River, 54

Watercress, on Shumagin Is-
    lands, 132, 135;
  as a cure for scurvy, 134, 136,
    146;

on Bering Island, 161
Waxel, Lieut., 67, 74-77;
  in council, 87, 154-156, 182-
    184;
  and Steller, 134-135, 140-144,
    161, 173;
  and scurvy, 161;
  takes command of expedition,
    173;
  returns to St. Petersburg, 210;
  later years of, 214
Whales, seen from *St. Peter*,
    101, 120, 127;
  parts of, used by Indians, 138-
    139, 142-143
Whortleberry, 120, 132
Wildcat, 12, 13, 16, 18, 26
Willow, 60, 178
Windsheim, 10, 14, 16, 17;
  burned, 28
Winter, at St. Petersburg, 39,
    40-42
  in Siberia, 44-45, 56-57, 61,
    64;
  in Alaska, 150;
  at sea, 151;
  on Bering Island, 172-173,
    176, 178-181, 204;
  sea cow in, 198
Wittenberg, city of, 10;
  University of, 21, 24-28, 37

Yakutsk, 64-65
Yeniseysk, 57
"Yezo," 81
Yushin, Second Mate, 77;
  and Steller, 92-94, 100;
  and scurvy, 152